Nicola Pagett trained at L............ ....er professional career at Worthing Repertory. She has appeared in the theatre, both in the West End and around the country, and also abroad in the United States. Numerous roles on television (including *Upstairs Downstairs*, *Anna Karenina*, *A Bit of a Do* and *Ain't Misbehavin'*) have brought her acclaim from a wide and varied audience.

Graham Swannell has written three stage plays which have been performed at the Lyric Hammersmith. The first of these plays, *A State of Affairs*, transferred to the Duchess theatre. In addition he has written over twenty radio plays.

They live in south-west London.

DIAMONDS BEHIND MY EYES

Nicola Pagett and Graham Swannell

With an Afterword
by Dr Desmond Kelly

VICTOR GOLLANCZ

LONDON

First published in Great Britain 1997
by Victor Gollancz
An imprint of the Cassell Group
Wellington House, 125 Strand, London WC2R 0BB

© Nicola Pagett and Graham Swannell 1997
Afterword © Desmond Kelly 1997

The right of Nicola Pagett and Graham Swannell
to be identified as authors of this work
has been asserted by them in accordance with
the Copyright, Designs and Patents Act, 1988.

A catalogue record for this book is
available from the British Library.

ISBN 0 575 06500 1

Typeset by Rowland Phototypesetting Ltd,
Bury St Edmunds, Suffolk
Printed and bound in Guernsey by
The Guernsey Press Co Ltd, Guernsey, Channel Isles

97 98 99 5 4 3 2 1

for Eve

1

I am an actress and I had a crack-up, breakdown, burn-out – what you will. I don't know if I qualify as famous, you never do. Once, years ago, laughing with an actor, he asked me, 'Are you international?'

'Nah,' I said. 'Are you?'

'Nope.'

Where did I go? I went where the air was too thin. I went up too high for too long. I went where you don't go.

I flew for five months.

It's autumn now and, as I look out of a window that needs cleaning, I wonder if I'm going to miss never being allowed to go there again.

Just before Christmas, I did something I'd never done before. I chased a part. I became absolutely single-minded about it. I wanted it so much and I couldn't get an interview. I followed it. It was offered – declined – offered again – declined again. I knew the director didn't want me, but it made no difference. I've worked with a knight who told me he didn't see the point of working where you weren't wanted. I agreed, but I couldn't stop.

'Give it away,' my husband said. 'Just give it away.'

I phoned my agent. It was uncast. I still had a chance.

The days rolled by. I couldn't stop thinking about it. I went into London, to the studio. We were doing a radio series – me and my chums. One of them always says, 'I'm a tart for laughs.' She'd had a baby four months before. He came too. He was so good while she went off to do a bit of acting. I looked after him sometimes. Then one morning she came in and said:

'I've been offered this part.'

'Oh,' I said. 'I wanted that.'

'Oh,' she said.

We didn't talk about it any more. It was horrible. I was trying so hard to be philosophical and all the rest of it, but I was really pissed off. What made it worse was that I really liked her and knew she'd be good in it.

The work was finished. We said *au revoir*. That's that, I thought.

Days passed. I was in the kitchen cooking supper and the phone rang and it was my chum.

'Darling, darling, ring your agent now! Ring your agent now this minute! I've just rung the theatre and told them I don't want to do it. I'm going to put the phone down now. OK? I'm putting the phone down.'

'Hang on, hang on a minute. What's up?'

'Oh, it's my thighs. They're too fat from the baby, and there's all that running about. I'm not sure any more. Maybe it's the baby, I'm not sure. Something's happened to my confidence. I don't know – I just don't want to do it any more.'

'Don't be daft. Have a go. They really want you.'

'I don't want to think about it any more,' she said. 'You've got to ring them now. Go on, otherwise it'll be too late.'

'Are you sure?'

'Yes, yes! Hurry up. Ring your agent.'

'Absolutely sure?'

'Yes, hurry up, or someone else will get it.'

I rang; more days to wait. More actresses turned it down.

And all the time the leading man had been pressing my case, saying he thought I was right for it, sending faxes to the theatre. I'd known him since the early seventies and I was fond of him. He believed in me. He'd defended me once when a director more or less implied I was rubbish. 'You're all right,' he said. 'She's all right – she's doing it right – what's your problem?'

At last I got an interview. They are never easy and this one was really difficult because I knew they were running out of casting time. I knew they didn't want me, but soon they might not have any choice. It was hard not to seem bolshie. I didn't talk too much, but when I did I went for broke and said how I really felt about the play and we agreed. We were in accord. She told me she was seeing one more actress.

Thirty-six more hours to wait. It was mine.

I felt when we started work that I'd forced myself on my director and I think she felt uncomfortable too, but it didn't last very long. She and I were in perfect harmony. It was we friends who began to fight. People think that's why I cracked up, but it isn't so. We'd argue in front of the cast.

'Don't give me orders,' I'd say.

'I'm not!'

'Yes you are.'

Then we'd phone each other after work.

'Darling, I'm so sorry,' we'd say.

One night, after yet another confrontation, my daughter shouted as I came through the door:

'He says he loves you!'

It was no use though. Mexican stand-off. We just didn't agree about the play. Our minds met at no point whatsoever. We saw the play from two different perspectives.

How strange that the director and I should be working in such peaceful accord, when she never wanted me in the first place. She seemed quite glad now. We had a shorthand. I knew what she was saying before she finished saying it. She took what I gave, refined it, and then returned it. I reciprocated.

I was working hard and there were so many other things in my head as well. The play was deeply political. I got very caught up in politics. Something was in the wind. Just a little breeze. The Labour Party was changing. Some of them liked it, some of them didn't. I wondered who'd win. But what did I know? I just got completely caught up in it. It was like history, only it wasn't in a book, it was live.

The rehearsal days were flicking by and there was so much to do. So many costume fittings, and people wanting to talk to me over lunch. I'd do my lines, but I'd listen to the news whenever I could as well; I didn't want to miss anything. I'd play music endlessly, and at home I stopped talking to my family.

There was so much to do. I had to read about the writer.

I had to write out poems from a book. Poems for everyone, for all the stage management as well. They were poems from a Chinese book – a book about horoscopes.

What was I doing? It seems such a strange thing to have done, but the funny thing was that no one found it odd then. Everyone really loved their poems. It took hours, and I should have been working calmly on the play, but I kept making myself do things.

There was no time, no time to rest.

But I couldn't rest. I didn't want to rest. I was so happy, we were so happy – companies usually are and this one certainly was.

Then I had to deal with something in the middle of rehearsals. I'd had lumps in my breasts for a few weeks. I had to go to the hospital. I'd been before, eleven years ago, and they'd taken them out and this time it was to be all right again. They were benign, but there's always that moment when the nurse puts the X-rays up on the screen. She puts the muscles in her face on hold. I watched her. She was the same nurse from all those years ago. We remembered each other. The doctor came in.

'I have to go back to work,' I said to the doctor. 'I can't take any time off work or anything.'

'We can fix it now,' she said. And she did.

She got out the syringe. It was such a long needle. She pushed it deep into my breast. It hurt. God, it hurt.

'Once more,' she said.

This time it went in so far, right through the nipple. She showed me all the golden liquid that had been inside me. I felt I'd gone right down, as far as you can go, or perhaps right up, into diamonds of pain.

I didn't go back to work that day.

The next day we had a row about my dress. It had to be hidden in the course of the play. I got cross with the actor when he stuffed it into his trousers.

'Hey!' I said. 'I've got to wear that in a minute. It'll be all creased!'

'I can't help that,' he said. 'I've got to put it somewhere.'

'Just don't squash it all up.'

'Leave it out.'

'Well, how would you like it if I put your dinner jacket in my knickers?'

And so it went on. We were always fighting and then making it all right again.

The actor was and is dear enough to have a row with, but it was a strain. The fighting, the needles and the play. How I loved the play, but I was so high all the time and so tired, and there was following the news to fit in as well. I'd read somewhere some Tory had said, 'Watch that man Blair.' It was so theatrical somehow, and anyway I got hooked on watching to see what would happen. And of course I couldn't sleep. I couldn't sleep and I couldn't stop.

2

Then everything changed in a split second.

I could tell the Stranger everything.

Everything was all right. Everything snapped into place.

I had seen his face on the screen. It was strong, beautiful even, but it wasn't that. He seemed somehow apart. As if he couldn't be bothered with the games people play.

I didn't really think about it though, I just went on with rehearsals. And then I saw his face among crowds of people, all busy, all going somewhere, and he looked so sad, so sad. The pain seemed to stretch back and back into his eyes. It was like an electric shock. I've seen that look before. There always seems to be resignation mixed up in it, but he didn't look resigned. He just looked as if he knew he had mountains to climb and he didn't know if he could make it.

Anyway he moved in and lived behind my eyes.

I didn't want to meet him. I didn't want anything. I just wanted to tell him how clever he was.

I remember sitting on a hard chair at the edge of the rehearsal room. There was a little explosion in my head. A voice whispered to me.

'It's meant. It's allowed. It's Valentine's Day tomorrow.'

It wasn't my thought. I knew I hadn't thought that thought. I knew – I knew – I knew. It had come from outside.

I found a card. It was a painting of a lady in a lacy white dress. A lady from a time before, sitting composedly at her desk writing, whilst at her shoulder a young man stood watching apprehensively. The man looked exactly like the Stranger. I turned the card over and wrote to him. I told him I was married and stole seven words that Charlotte Brontë wrote in the middle of *Jane Eyre*: 'God keep you from harm and wrong.'

But then I couldn't stop. I couldn't stop writing letters. I sent him a cheque for six billion pounds, and signed it, 'Moi'.

Then I sent him a card of a cartoon. It was Snow White, looking a little ropy. It said, 'I *was* Snow White but I drifted.' I cut some black lace from a pair of knickers, pasted it very lightly to the card, perfumed it and wrote:

Please remove

Underneath it said in very tiny letters:

Tories is berks
And nobody werks.

I didn't know I was sick. All I knew was that I felt so good when the pen sped across the pages. I wrote about everything. How I felt about everything. I told him about the needles. I told him I'd read somewhere that there'd been an experiment in a laboratory. They'd done an experiment with a woman's tears. They'd rescued two tears. One from a woman peeling onions and one from another as she wept. The first tear was salt water but the second had morphine in it. The article said that pain and stress release morphine. You make your own.

I told the Stranger that, at the hospital, when they were putting the needles away, they'd said to me:

'You're supposed to cry.'

'I don't want to cry,' I said. 'I feel quite calm really, because of the morphine.'

They looked at me as if I were mad. But it was interesting. Why didn't they find it, at the very least, interesting?

I wrote to the Stranger: 'Please tell me to stop if you don't like this. I'd hate it if someone kept writing to me. Please tell me.'

No word came. So I went on. I told him about an actor who always wore his pyjamas when he took his little boy to school. The other children hadn't found it odd because they knew his father didn't have a proper job.

I told him that I thought my daughter was bright, because years ago, when she was three, she'd said to me: 'If you give me some money I'll let you read to me.'

I told him about a winter afternoon at boarding school when some players came to do Shakespeare. How it had been a bit boring and over my head, but the striding about in swishy cloaks was good and so were the pointing fingers.

We'd had our supper and coming back from chapel I watched them having theirs – they'd taken over our common room. I'd stared. They were so irreverent. I wanted to be let in, I wanted to be part of it. I wanted to eat supper with my shoes off and make a mess and smoke. I watched them for a long time, wondering why exactly the room looked so different. I'd never seen my school from outside the window looking in. It was cold outside and the window steamed up. What had the players done to it? They'd changed it. I sat there every day with the others after lunch, the silent time before games. Sweets allowed and quiet reading. The room was different, the lights were golden. They'd moved the furniture and it was friendly. They talked so loud.

'Darling!' someone screamed.

The plates weren't stacked and had cigarette ash on them and smears of leftover butter. When we had supper, we took it in turns to divide the butter, one line lengthways and four across. There was never any left over.

There were men among the girls, their voices all mixed up. One girl was holding on to the table, rocking on her chair and laughing. I watched for ages. They looked very disobedient. They looked like bandits.

They were alight.

3

The play opened.

I had to write all my entrances on a piece of paper and stick it to the back of the set, otherwise I'd get in a muddle. I found it confusing but no one seemed worried.

I dropped the top of the whisky bottle on the first night. It rolled down the desk. It wasn't fatal, but it was an irritating, incompetent mistake to have made. It worried the audience for some seconds. Little things like that are disquieting, but all in all it was a success, and I said it all and in the right order.

There was a do afterwards and then we all went dancing. I danced with my husband. Everything was perfect.

I had two worlds. I had the play, music, writing and dancing. God how I danced. You name it – I danced it. *Swan Lake*, Scottish reels, Irish jigs, and general jumping about *circa* 1968. I could not stop.

Then there was the other world, the real world. The world where other people lived. I was beginning to like it less and less. I had to concentrate and pay attention so that I could understand what they were saying to me. But it was tiring with such a fizzy head. So I went back to the first world.

I loved my part.

I loved it more than any part I'd ever played. I loved the language. The merciless, exquisite English that Orton used. I loved the irreverence, the wit and the sex. It was a play entirely without guilt. There was joy in it too. It was England as it used to be before the Victorians changed us.

I loved my clothes – especially when I took them off.

I've always wanted the sort of hair that would flop all over my face to order, and they'd made me a wig that did exactly that. I loved coming through the door in leopardskin and sunglasses, and I loved the spiky shoes, the black stocking tops and lots and lots of very red lipstick.

This play had everything. Wit, sex, fighting, screaming, love and a gun. They had done us proud in the armoury department. The gun didn't make the usual ineffectual stage pop – these sounded like real bullets. It was heavy in my hand and when I fired it pictures fell off walls and radios exploded. The fire extinguisher spat foam all over the place.

I loved waiting in the wings with a stagehand – wearing my black slip – waiting to fire my gun. The light made my skin go gold. I felt beautiful and powerful. There was sex in the air, but it was confused because I had the gun. We never spoke. I had to keep an eye on the cue light. It was shadowy and the red bulb flicked on and off very fast.

We were waiting for green. The play roared, on the other side of the door, but we were still, concentrating.

He gave me a scrap of torn white cardboard to weave in and out of my hair – to double as a piece of fallen plaster. I never said thank you. It would have spoilt it to speak. So we never spoke and we never looked at each other.

Perhaps he looked at me when I kicked the door open. He must have done because he had to throw brick-dust all over me. He was high up on a ladder in the wings. Seconds later I would have to run – fast – back into the wings to dip my hands into a bowl of blood. It felt warm and it trickled down the insides of my arms. Then the loudest scream I could manage and back on stage again. The actor struck my face and I put my hand up to touch my cheek. Blood and lipstick and hair all over my face. Then he threw me to the ground. The floor tore my stockings. The bra strap fell down. It felt great. The exhaustion and the freedom of it all.

Now I really am relaxed, I thought. Now I am walking properly across the back of this stage because I am too tired to be tense.

I was allowed to be a woman in a man's world, but on my terms, not theirs. I was allowed to do what men do, but I could wear torn black stockings while I did it. I could be part of what was exciting and dangerous, but on my terms. It was the perfect part.

He showed us how to do it, the fight arranger, he taught us. Us girls in the play. It was hard to remember. It had to be precise.

'Is it, push – kick – shove – down?' I asked. 'Or push – shove – kick – down?'

'No, it's push – shove – hold – kick – down,' he said. 'Do it again.'

We got better. We got good. We could do it really fast after a few runs at it. So fast. It looked real but it was planned. It was meticulous, so meticulous that it looked spontaneous.

I loved my part.

Perhaps I like being thrown about. Perhaps I find violence exciting. Perhaps, but I'm not sure.

When I was ten my mother made me a party dress. I adored it. Blue taffeta with filmy, slippery white material over it and it had a sash. The dress would rustle. It would whisper to me in my bedroom. I remember feeling floaty and different. I went to the party. But the feeling wore off – the whispery ladylike feeling. I couldn't do anything. I couldn't move in case I got dirty. I had to stand about being ladylike. Every part of me felt stiff and separate. The next party I went to I took a change of clothes. I took my shorts and a top. Half-way through I'd nip up and change.

We used to play a wonderful game called jacks when I was ten. It involved a rubber ball and ten little metal things rather like sputniks. It needed dexterity. You threw them up and caught them on the back of your hand, throwing the ball up with your other hand. The game progressed. First you picked up one, that was easy. It got hard when you had to pick up ten in one go.

You had to kneel on the ground to play. Carpets were no good and wooden floors unsuitable, it had to be hard ground. I liked the freedom of dirty knees. I liked the bits of grit that got embedded in the skin. I liked the feel of the bumps as I ran my fingers over my knees. I liked playing as it got dark. It was so still. My bike propped up.

'I'll go home in a minute.'

The ground was so cool against my legs, against my skin. I was quite alone. I played by myself. I was the game. I was the ground. I was the light getting darker.

When I fought in the play, when everything got confused and broken, when I got untidy and my clothes got torn, it felt the same as being ten. It felt the same as being out too late on my bike, coasting with no hands, hot and dirty, then speeding up and taking corners at too sharp an angle. I could get the pedal to scrape the ground. At school there was a slope with a little ditch separating it from where we played. The ditch was irrelevant if you took it really fast. Even when you blew it, it was worth it. When you did fall off, the moment before gave you such a rush.

I fell in love with speed, I suppose. I like going too fast. The play was like that. It made me feel I was going too fast. But what bliss never to be bored, never for an instant.

When the curtain came down, we'd be happy, the six of us, as we climbed the stairs and wandered down corridors to get cleaned up. You could see across the courtyard into other dressing rooms. Sometimes the actor would give me a lightning flash as he changed. We'd stopped fighting.

4

I can't remember exactly when the Stranger put a camera in the mirror.

It was there, though, and only he could decide whether he watched me alone, or with other people.

I didn't mind. I liked it.

I'd take off my bloodstained slip, my wig and the torn stockings. Sometimes only one would have a ladder in it, so I'd hold the other one up and say, 'Waste not, want not.'

I liked it when he watched me take my make-up off. I loved washing the blood from my throat, from my arms and from my breasts. Sometimes there would be blood on my thighs and I'd smile into the mirror as I made myself clean again.

All the time I had the music on, unless, of course, it was news time. I watched all the newses. If it was about Northern Ireland. I taught the Stranger the accent.

'Mossis Totcher, Mossis Totcher.'

There were always candles. I loved the light.

It was such a small room, like a womb. I'd made it mine though, with Blu-tacked posters, and paper sunflowers.

Even though I didn't want to, I had to leave it sometimes. I'd put on my green dressing-gown and go and buy carrot cake and coffee. I'd eat it, and then try to sleep. I had always been able to sleep between shows before, but not now, not any more.

'You have to dance,' the Stranger said.

Then it would be time to do the show all over again. The Stranger would watch me as I got made up once more. The designer had set the play in the sixties so I knew exactly how to do my eyes. It needs a steady hand to get that smooth slanting line to finish neatly at a sharp point.

'Go on then,' he'd say. 'Do the other one the same.'

And I would. I took hours putting on the black stockings. He liked those, he really liked those. He even liked them with no legs in them. I used to wave them about. He liked what the padding did to my bosom. He could see it was a con but he didn't mind.

Time would tick on, it was time to work. I was hooked into the black, my skin sliding against the silk. My place was tidy and I swapped my cigarette for chewing gum.

There was a cloud of scent.

'Beginners on stage, please.'

Slippers off, spiky shoes on, shut the door. Click clack, click clack down the hall.

'Damn!'

The suspender's come adrift again. There's no one about, just his camera. Lift everything up, fix it. I sense him smile.

Open the double doors and grin at all the girls sewing on the other side of the window. They're chatting and sipping tea. Down more steps. My legs look quite nice. I wonder what he thinks? More doors and then I'm in the darkened wings.

Hush. The play is in the middle distance.

I check in the dark mirror lit with a single lamp. I look great. I can't see anything.

'Don't think you're good,' I tell myself. 'You'll blow it. Don't think you're bad, you're not. Don't think anything. Breathe.'

All those lines in my head, pages and pages of them.

'Are they? Don't think. Breathe. Sit and wait. Am I any good? I know their lines, do I know mine? Don't think, don't think.'

It's getting nearer. It's time to stick my chewing gum behind the vase. I sit straight with my feet together.

The red light is flashing. I walk towards it slowly and press it. The red light stills, I wait for green.

'Remember you have time, on stage and off. Concentrate.'

I put my hand on the doorknob. Nearly time, no way back. Green.

Go.

Step through, out and into white light and say the first line.

'Who are you talking to?' I'd say.

I was on. I was her. I was home.

Sometimes I wondered if the Stranger ever watched the play on his camera. I wondered what he thought.

I can't remember when he put the tiny little James Bond microphone in my left ear. He'd put it in my ear. I never wondered how or why. I just knew it was there, because when I lifted up a steel chair by chance one day, there was interference on the radio.

'You have to have it so that I can always talk to you wherever you are,' he said.

Neither can I remember when the Stranger bugged the house, nor how he put the cameras in place, but one day they were just there.

First they were in the bedroom and then all over the house.

I saw my American neighbour getting into her car one morning and she gave me a funny look. I knew she'd put a camera in my car too, because both she and the Stranger were American.

The camera was filming me as I drove and we'd share the music. Then I realized I was being filmed in the loo. I didn't go to the lavatory for three days. I couldn't get away from him and the cameras. When I turned the light out in my dressing-room bathroom, I heard him whisper:

'Infra-red.'

He could see me everywhere. I had to go to the loo downstairs at the theatre and not use the one in the dressing room.

At home in the conservatory when I played him my LPs I found he'd changed all the words. He'd had someone steal into my house, take all my records away and change them. The lyrics were different.

At first I didn't mind about the cameras in the bedroom but when I realized they were all over the house, even in the loo – I begged him to take them away. Over and over I'd ask him.

'Please take them away. Please take them away.'

'Just give me three more days,' he said.

But he never took them away.

Then the people on the radio could hear me as well, they could see me too, as I dressed and undressed. I used to hide from the people on the radio and the Stranger behind the cupboard. Then, one day, I heard him whisper:

'You forgot the mirror.'

I realized that they could see me everywhere.

I was doing my yoga one morning and in one of the exercises you stretch your legs right out wide. I distinctly remember Terry Wogan saying:

'We see what you mean.'

I felt guilty. Doing something so suggestive.

The Stranger watched me as I slept. He could see me but I couldn't see him except behind my eyes. I knew he didn't love me as I loved him. It didn't matter somehow, he cared enough to watch me. I didn't mind, I really didn't mind. I just wished him well in his work. I wanted him to win the day. I wanted him to win in spades. It wasn't about having a love affair. You need time for love and he didn't have any. It wasn't like that. I just wanted the sadness to leave his eyes.

'Can you sleep?' I asked him once.

'Yes,' he said. 'I sleep fine, surprisingly well in fact.'

I was a bit miffed then. I cheered up, though, when the song on the radio said to turn it round. To turn the radio round because the camera wasn't pointing straight.

The days passed. I can't remember very clearly. The builders were making me a front garden. I fed them walnut cake. I fed the birds. I talked to the Stranger all the time, in the garden, in the house, and I didn't sleep.

'Do you know you're talking to yourself?' my husband said.

It wasn't worth discussing.

One afternoon I walked from the theatre to the railway station to post one of my endless letters. I'd written a sketch. I'd watched so much news, I'd written a parliamentary sketch.

'Order! Order! Mr Blair.'

'Madam Speaker, is it not the case that this country would be better served if the party opposite fucked off out of it?'

'Order! Order! Mr Blair! I really cannot have this. Would the right honourable gentleman care to rephrase his comments?'

'I would simply like to say, Madam Speaker, that the party opposite is comprised chiefly of a load of old wankers and the country is fed up with them. Also, Madam Speaker, may I now pre-empt what the right honourable gentleman will reply to my comments? He will witter on about my soundbites, which are bloody hard to think up, and then he will say, Madam Speaker, he will say, "Clearly, Madam Speaker, the party opposite is so desperate it continues to practise the politics of envy."'

'Order! Order! The Prime Minister.'

'Clearly, Madam Speaker, clearly the party opposite, clearly, is so clearly desperate, that it clearly continues to clearly practise the politics of envy – clearly.'

'Hear hear! Bollocks bollocks! Hear hear!'

'Order, order! The Prime Minister.'

'Thank you, Madam Speaker. We in the Conservative Party are proud to be a load of old wankers. Wanking is a fine old British tradition and I will not have it traduced and denigrated in this way. And may I say, Madam Speaker, is it not typical of the party opposite to take every opportunity to undermine all that we hold dear.'

'Jolly good, well said.'

'I'll second that.'

'Oooh, you'd never guess the PM's only read one book.'

'Which book's that?'

'*Let's Sell the Railways and Buy Our Coal From Venezuela.*'

'Order, order! Mr Blair.'

'Madam Speaker, we on this side of the House are the first to affirm and support fine old British traditions but we maintain, Madam Speaker, that wanking is the chief source of unemployment in society today. We would suggest to the right honourable gentleman and his right honourable friends that making love is the order of the day. We want to get our country back to work.'

'Rubbish! Cobblers!'

'Madam Speaker, we want to see full employment.'

'Yeah, man! Rock on Tony!'

'Who's going to pay for it? Eh? Eh? Who's going to pay? Who's going to foot the bill?'

'Oh, shut it! You always say that. It's so boring.'

'Order, order! Mr Portillo.'

'Madam Speaker, I would just like to point out at this point that my hair is shinier than anyone else's, and I am extremely smooth and charming, and I would make a very poncey prime minister.'

'Fuck off! Leave it out!'

'Order! ORDER!'

'Let him speak!'

'NO!'

'This is a democracy!'

(Biff)

'No it isn't!'

'Don't waffle, Mr Portillo. What is your question?'

'Why can't I be Prime Minister?'

'Sit down. SIT DOWN! If you don't sit down, Mr Portillo – WILL you sit down? No? May I have a volunteer? Would a right honourable member please sit on Mr Portillo? Thank you, Mr Lilley. Let him breathe, Mr Lilley. We don't want to starve him of the oxygen of publicity.'

(Bang. Bang. Bang)

'Shit – sorry – bloody hell – fuck me!'

'Down everyone, GET DOWN! It's Norman Lamont! He's got a gun. It's a .22.'

'Bloody hell!'

'Lord love a duck.'

'What?'

'Cripes! I'm going to become killed!'

'Who said that?'

'The PM.'

'God almighty! Mr Prescott, would you mind sorting this out?'

'Certainly, Madam Speaker. Now Norman, give me the gun.'

'Shan't.'

'Come on, give me the gun.'

'Jolly well shan't. Oh, John . . .'

(Little sob)

'Now, Norm, I know it's unfair. We all know it's unfair.

We all know you offered to resign before you got the elbow.'

(Louder sobs)

'We love you really.'

(Even louder sobs)

'Come on, pull yourself together. Take it like a man. You never know, it might get better. It isn't looking very good – but you never know. Do you want to borrow a tenner? There's an off-licence round the corner.'

(Exit Norman Lamont)

I posted this to the Stranger at the station.

I hoped it might make him laugh.

As I walked round the station there were messages for me everywhere.

A train for the Isle of Wight meant a girlfriend who lived there was saying hello. Post Office advertisements meant the Stranger wanted my letters. A child being sick was to remind me of a time when my daughter got carsick. I was all-seeing. I noticed everything. The station looked like a set and all the people there were part of the film. Of course all the time I was being filmed too.

The Stranger wanted to buy me some yellow tulips. I kept one of the petals when the flowers died. I balanced it on the candle when it was unlit, when I was on-stage, and I took it with me on tour in my make-up case. It was so romantic of him to buy me flowers.

I don't think I've ever been so happy.

There was music all day long and music all through the night, even in the bedroom. I was sleeping by myself because I couldn't sleep without the music. No one could stop me playing the radio all night. I couldn't turn it off once I'd turned it on, because if I did whoever was singing would know, and then their feelings would be hurt. I knew if I turned the radio on I'd have to go on listening – anything else would be so rude. If I had to do anything I'd have to wait for an advertisement and then switch off very fast. I'd doze till three in the morning – always three – and then I'd get up and go down to the kitchen.

One night Charles Aznavour was singing, so I danced with him. That night I needed no light, because the full moon lit up the kitchen.

5

The Stranger came to call.

He had turned into a blackbird.

The Labour Party were sparrows and starlings and the Tories were pigeons. I'm not overfond of Tories or pigeons and I spent half an hour running all over the garden, frightening them in my dressing-gown. I'd put the sponge-cake crumbs out for the Labour Party, but the pigeons kept taking everything. It got quite nasty. One pigeon wasn't scared of me. Just for a second I thought of its sharp beak. It would fly away but come back almost immediately. I ran out of puff eventually and went back into the kitchen. Then I heard it. I heard it clacking about on the PVC roof of the conservatory. I tiptoed to the cupboard and got the broom out. I crept back and bashed the roof with the handle. Mrs Thatcher took off in a hell of a hurry.

But the blackbird was so sweet and tame and brave. My husband said he'd seen him fight off a magpie. I wondered if he knew too that the Stranger was a blackbird. I didn't ask him though.

All I knew was I'd crossed over to a place where being

alive was like being on fire. Everything was unbearably, unutterably beautiful. I didn't need my husband any more. There were the cameras to talk to and the radio people to take care of me. I started burning newspaper for the cameras in the house opposite. I'd come home from the show and go straight into the kitchen. I don't know what I was worked up about one night but I made a newspaper torch and set fire to it over the sink.

'What are you doing?' asked my husband.

'Burning newspaper.'

'Why?'

'What do you mean why? I'll clear it up. What's the problem?'

'Oh, God,' he said. 'Just come next door now and sit down.'

'I will, I will – I'll come in a minute,' I said. 'I just want to watch *Newsnight*.'

'No!' he said. 'Come now, you're getting all hyped up. I've had enough of *Newsnight*.'

'Sshh – they'll hear you.'

'Who will?'

'They've bugged the house.'

'You're getting paranoid,' he said. 'There's something about that in this book I'm reading.'

'I'm not going to live my life because of some fucking book!' I yelled at him.

'Oh Christ, I give up,' he said and went off to bed.

I needed to rest too, to sleep because of the show, but I couldn't. Vivien Leigh had this. In his biography, Sir Laurence calls her his 'no sleep baby'. The Stranger was with me all the time. He'd ask the people on the radio to talk to me and they did.

One night I heard my own voice coming back to me. I must have been dozing because it woke me up. I was calling his name. It was so high-pitched, almost like keening. I got out of bed and saw the lights in the windows of the house opposite flash on and off – on and off – on and off – over and over and over again. It was golden light that lit up the sky.

I went downstairs. I was hungry. I'd been very worried about an Englishman called Nick, in prison in Alabama for killing someone. Every day it was on the news. They were going to electrocute him. They were – they weren't – they were – they weren't. No one in the government had said anything, not even that they felt for his family. I felt I was in Alabama with him – waiting with him. And then they killed him. They strapped him into a chair and they fried him alive. I made a newspaper torch and held it up high for the cameras. Then I drank his health with a glass of Margaux. Somehow the wine turned into blood. I also lit a cigarette. I knew they were hysterical about smoking in America. I put some Schubert on and said as loud as I dared:

'Hey you, Alabama! Bastards! Fucking bastards! Thou shalt not kill. It's in the bloody book. Thou shalt not kill. And another thing, Vengeance is mine, saith the Lord. Mine, not yours. Vengeance is mine, mine, mine. How I hate you, fucking Alabama!'

I got a bit peckish then so I fried an egg and ate it on a piece of toast with a cup of tea.

My husband asked in the morning whether I'd been up

in the night. I told him what I'd done, about frying the egg and Nick.

'That's horrible,' he said.

'No, it's not,' I answered. 'It was a funeral bakemeat.'

I told him I was so proud of Nick, because before he died he'd spat at the man strapping him in. He'd been English – he'd been one of ours and he hadn't cowered. And why the fuck hadn't there been some spitting when they'd threatened to murder Salman Rushdie? Eh? He was one of ours too. Or maybe they didn't see it like that.

There were no laughs that day, but one morning I did make him laugh. I bounced into the spare room at 5.30.

'I slept. I slept. I didn't wake up!' I said. 'Aren't you pleased?'

We laughed. We were together, but only for a second. I couldn't stay there with him, something must have happened to my will. I had no will any more – the radio people and the Stranger and the music kept pulling me away.

My husband was going further and further away and the Stranger was coming nearer and nearer.

6

I wrote at night.

In the early hours, I used to creep out in the dark to post the letters, in my bedsocks. Well, not just in my bedsocks, in my night attire.

I'd told the Stranger about my bedsocks. They said 'Merry Christmas'. They still say 'Merry Christmas'. I thought there was a taxi waiting round the corner and that the driver had a key to the postbox. He'd only take my letter away when I wasn't looking. It was so still and cold and quiet in the street. There was only me.

I wrote a poem about queens and bedsocks and unworthy questions.

I wrote of blinding rage. I'd read that Nestlé had been selling their powdered milk to the Third World. The mothers in the villages had thought that their babies would grow to be as bonny as western ones, but they used dirty river water to mix the milk and all the babies died.

I didn't want to seem morbid all the time so I told him a story. I told him about the little flaxen-haired moppet, who had been allowed to play with the builders as they worked outside her house. The builders didn't mind at all.

She had her own little wheelbarrow and was singing her own little song.

'Are you doing some building, dear?' asked an old lady passing by.

'No, the fucking bricks haven't come, have they.'

At the theatre I was having such a good time. The audiences were so responsive and some very ritzy people were coming.

I was getting bolder for the cameras. I talked to the cue light when the others were on-stage. It was the Stranger's special camera – just for we two. I'd talk to him in the wings. Play tricks with the light – go right up close and give it a kiss. Sometimes the Stranger would watch the show.

I was also getting bolder for the camera in the dressing room. I think I've always been modest and I think I've always hated being stared at. Perhaps those days were numbered now. Perhaps I'd wasted years and years minding when men looked at me. I was going to miss this. So I got bolder for the cameras – what I wore, what I didn't wear in the dressing room. I felt like an actress. I felt tacky and tarty and I liked it. Maybe actresses like being tarts. Maybe tarts like being actresses.

I was going up and up. I was going so high. What I felt – what I saw – what I said – was being beamed world-wide. There was no question of it not being so. It was explosive – everyone could see. We must all help each other – the whole world. I had to get in touch with the whole world with the cameras in the house opposite to help me. I had to reach everyone in all the countries.

So I looked in the kitchen cupboards and found I had

food from all over the world. There was soy sauce for China and Japan, curry powder for India, lumpfish for Russia. (I didn't have any caviar or vodka.) There was butter for New Zealand, maple syrup for Canada and American mustard. Pickles for Poland, tortilla chips for Mexico and a frozen croissant for France.

I got a bit stuck with Tibet.

But then I had a brainwave. Everyone lived till about 130 in Tibet, I'd read it somewhere, all they ate was yoghurt and apricots. I had both.

There were candles on the windowsill and music. I always played *Imagine* when the world was involved. My daughter gave me a little ladybird – a little metallic ladybird, to bring me luck when I went on tour. I turned him into John Lennon. And I had another tiny black something which was Elvis. I used to make them dance, right up close to the camera in my hotel room.

I lost the ladybird. It got burnt. I balanced it in the rim of the candle and it melted. I've lost so many things. I lost my worry beads from Corfu.

'Why don't you use your mum's glass beads?' whispered the Stranger.

I lost my Mac pink lipstick and I couldn't be bothered to flog all the way into Harvey Nic's to get another one.

I was still doing the show. How? I don't know. Danger – how I must have loved the danger of it all. I never knew I was living so close to the edge. There must have been the stray thought – easily crushed – that such a lovely part in such a lovely theatre – such silly sweet actors to act with – was too good to be true. I was burning up with joy. It was early spring.

I was only forty-nine and the Stranger was there all the time – taking care of me. I could think anything and it would be true.

I knew the Stranger was kind because once, in the early hours, when the music was making me cry, I heard him say:

'It's all right, dearie. It's all right – it's all right.'

As I've never used the word 'dearie' in my life, and have never even thought the word 'dearie', I knew he was there, because I heard his voice. I knew that he cared that I missed my mother, ten long years dead.

I think I was an angry little girl. I don't know why. Perhaps I was confused. I must be among the last children of a child of the Empire and so I led a double life.

'No horseplay in the drawing room.'

How you looked and how well you behaved were what counted and you had a place, you were a child. But in the streets and in the little wooden house with matting floors and slatted paper doors, wearing a kimono, none of that seemed important. There, people seemed so glad to see you and you were equal. My skin was white, theirs wasn't. In my world we were separate, but crossing to theirs we were the same.

Further back I remember Egyptian love – Black Nanny. I think I remember squashy black arms that scooped you up and wrapped you round. Arms that didn't pull away because they enjoyed the embrace as much as you did. Dark skin spelt love. Love in no hurry. I think I remember that, but I don't.

I do remember being twelve and landing in a propeller plane that flew me east to west to boarding school. I remember a high-ceilinged room with a fan, cool tiles and mosquito nets and a lady in a sari. She wasn't in a hurry either. She stayed and stayed and sent me off to sleep with a musky, dusky Indian kiss.

Vivien Leigh was born in India. She was only six when she was sent to an English boarding school. There was one thing, reading about her, that had seared itself into my memory. When she took her knickers off at night she used to place a clean hanky over them.

I worked with her in 1965 when I was nineteen. There was a revolve and we used to sit together waiting to come round to play the scene. Always the same lighting, a golden spotlight would catch her face – the side of her face. There were no lines any more. She looked so young, and her sadness seemed quieter. At the same point in the play, every night, her beauty took my breath away. I thought, I'm going to say it. So I did.

'You're so beautiful.'

She didn't look at me. She didn't smile and she didn't frown. It was as if it were irrelevant.

When I went to boarding school you were only given clean knickers on Wednesdays and Saturdays. I like clean knickers every day, so I'd wash mine myself, but I could never get them to dry on the brown radiators that were never hot so I'd wear them still damp.

7

I thought there was a pool of pain in the world.

A pool constantly being refilled with pain so the water had to be drunk to keep the world from overflowing. Drinking more than your share meant you lessened someone else's pain. Perhaps the poets and musicians and Van Gogh, who help so much, drink too deeply.

It was all right to live there so long as no one tried to stop me. If they tried to stop me I got nasty.

I've always known what love is ever since I was small. I've always known it was for better or worse. But I forgot. I pushed them away, those who loved me, my husband and my daughter. I hardly spoke to them and when I did it was brusque, clipped. They weren't real. I couldn't see them, there was something in the way and they wouldn't let me listen to my music. It didn't seem loud to me.

The music was real. The play was real. The dressing room was real. That was where I was closest to the Stranger. That was where we lived. I gave him the other half of my sandwich once because I'd had enough.

I lived where the cameras could see me even as I slept. Sometimes though it would get too much. It was too intense because I didn't have a minute's privacy. At the theatre I'd turn the cue light round so the Stranger couldn't see me.

'Take the cameras away,' I'd say. 'Take the cameras away!'

My work began to be affected. Towards the end of the play I had to scream, 'I am mad!' So I'd scream the line and then whisper into the microphone in my ear.

'See, cleverclogs,' I'd breathe. 'You thought that was real – but I was only acting.'

Then I'd miss my cue but I was getting away with it.

At home I went on writing. I told the Stranger how achingly beautiful the sky was and that I thought sunsets were trailers for death. I told him that I thought right was infinitely more powerful than wrong. I told him I wanted to give puppies to the boys who killed the toddler. Supervised, of course, and they'd have to clear up the mess in the exercise yard. I wanted to show them that it was just as easy to love something small and helpless as it was to hurt it.

I was losing it then but I didn't know.

'They're not proper Tories,' I kept muttering. 'They're not like Lord Carrington or Mr Biffen. They're not proper Tories. They stole my country and then they sold it. They sold it cheap, back to the people it belonged to. It wasn't theirs to sell.'

I had two obsessions. I thought the Falklands War had started because Denis Thatcher had business interests there in guano. I thought the Maastricht opt-out was a deal between us and Germany to agree to the recognition of Croatia. I thought dying for an opt-out was bad enough, but dying for birdshit?

I had so much hate in me. I went into the heart of hate. That's what it felt like. I hated the people who hit babies:

'You're not slapping them – you're not smacking them and it's not good. They're not good smacks or good slaps. You're hitting them. You're punching them. You're teaching them – you're teaching them to be as vicious and as violent as you are.'

I hated the mother who'd allowed a childminder to hit her children when she wasn't there. I hated the judge who'd condoned it.

I'd hit my daughter once. It was a release. When I realized that, I wanted to go somewhere and be sick, but I couldn't even do that. I never hit her again.

One night the hate bubbled up and I couldn't stop it spilling all over the kitchen – all over the music – all over everything beautiful. Everywhere was hate – everything was hate. I was shaking with it.

'Fucking bitch mothers – fucking cows – fucking sacred cows. We've been fucking up the world for millennia. Go on – hit him – again – harder – go on – discipline – that's what we like. There he stands in his short trousers – stunned. Take them down while you're at it – take everything away from him – what does he need with his manhood? He thought he'd got something right – but he made a mistake – didn't he? Can't have that. Hit him again – then dry his tears – he adores you – he loves you – even as you hit him – and you know that – don't you? Bitch! God, how you love the power of love. It's the only power you've got – the power of love. But you're a lazy sacred cow – aren't you? So lazy. You can't be bothered to go through hours of outraged yelling at no sweets – no television – although you know it works. It's easier just to hit him – and it's fun – and you feel so much better. After all, you're St Mother, aren't you? Bitch. Bitch. Bitch. Make him hate women the way you hate men.'

We were walking down a street one day – me and my old man. There was a woman at the bus stop hitting her little boy so hard – so hard. He went up to her.

'Don't do that.'

I've never loved him so much.

It had to be a man. A man had to say that. If I'd said it there would have been a nasty undignified scene. But the woman did exactly what she was told. Men just have it – when push comes to shove, men just have it. The authority.

I remembered a steel door. I remembered seeing a priest standing in front of a boarded-up council flat in Westminster. It was sealed up so that they could sell the property to Tory voters.

'This is wrong. It is wrong!'

I loved the priest for saying that, for being brave.

I was so tired and burning up so fast. Always I needed to dance at night in the kitchen and smoke and drink coffee. The more coffee I drank, the more I needed it to stay up. Up – Up – Up.

I'd waltz round the world.

'Hello,' I'd say. '*Bonjour – Aloha – Buon giorno – Skol – Prosim – Guten Morgen – G'day – Hi – Dobriden – Ohiogozaemas – Buenos días – Sukran – Litraut – Ya'sou –* Peking duck.'

I didn't know hello in Chinese.

I remembered a restaurant in Shanghai and then I was there. It had red velvet curtains and my little sister and I carried a Chinese baby all the way round the room. Chinese smiles.

We were never still when I was small. I was born in Egypt; thence at three to Cyprus, and on to Hong Kong (and all ports in between). At five, we sailed to Yokohama, and a Catholic convent school, where I stayed till I was twelve; then on a ship to England, to boarding school in Bexhill. Backwards and forwards every summer via Anchorage, Alaska. There were so many ships. They all merge into one and they were home too. Friends in the cabin, stewards with drinks and saying goodbye. Then the 'get off the ship' bell would clang and all the people would swing down the gangplank to stand on the dock.

I saw their faces looking up as they waited for the ship to move. Bustle and commotion. Then the hooter whooped and we threw the paper streamers down, holding one end whilst they caught the other. You unwound the paper for as long as you could, and as the ship and shore drew further and further apart, you leant forward trying to make the streamer stretch. Then there was the tearing sound as the paper ripped and fell into the sea. The people were dots and it was the end. It was quick and it was sharp, all the faces gone.

But ship life was beginning. It was time to suss things out. Slipping away unnoticed, I was never caught. In twenty minutes it was sorted. The distance between the decks – how far from stem to stern – right up to the bridge, and then right down again, down to the engine room. Hiding and watching what they did. Metal clashing and pumping noises, and men in vests with shiny arms who didn't know I was there, and the hot oily smell.

Then back to the cabin and on the way the ship smell. The smell of salt and rust and paint. Turning on the taps in the little bathroom. One for seawater, one for fresh. Turn it off, don't waste it, turn it off. There'll be nothing left to drink, I thought.

One afternoon it rained and I felt shut in the ship.

'I've got to get out!'

There was no one about and I shouldn't have been there. There were ropes across everywhere because it was so rough. The deck was awash with rain and sea. I skated my way to the front of the main deck and looked – it was a long way down. The line of the ship was so sharp, the curve so pleasing. The ship was like a carving-knife cutting the waves in two.

I stayed a long time holding tight to the metal rails – so wet and cold and rough, where the paint had rusted in little flakes. Then the wind got up.

I bet I can hold harder than the wind can blow.

The ship went right up in the air and then right down again, fighting the water and winning. It was like being on a horse and galloping slowly. I felt very tall. I felt very close to something important, holding on so tight. The rain was like kisses and the wind blew cool underneath my hair. I felt the glory of God.

God was King of the Wind and the Waves and I was Queen of the Sea.

If I fall in, I'll die and I'll be all by myself. I'll have to watch the ship getting smaller and smaller. Will my ears go pop before I am dead?

I want my mum.

No you don't. You'll get found out and you won't be

allowed to come up here to feel the feeling. It's time to go. I'll be all right if I run straight and too fast to slip.

Anyway, I've had enough of the feeling for the moment. I want to get back to the game. I'll round up the kids on the ship and we'll finish it. I've got Mayfair and Park Lane. I've got my 'Get out of jail free' card, and some of my stash left. Roll the dice.

Seeing land, that was a magical feeling. A sliver of shade on the horizon.

Where are we now? What will I see? Brown men sitting on bales, eating curry with one hand? Palm trees floating past the ship? Ropes, sunshine, tugs? The big white ship couldn't enter the port by itself. Little brown tugs would pull it into the harbour. The big white ship just sat there and the tugs did all the work. The big ship couldn't manage it, but it never thanked the little tugs. Then the big fat ropes tied us to the dock.

Looking up from the swinging gangplank.

'What are those for?' I asked my dad.

'What?'

'Those steel saucers at the tops of the ropes?'

'They're to stop the rats getting on board.'

Once in the East we were allowed to throw money in the water. That was when the ship came to rest among all the brown junks with flapping sails. Everyone on the little boats seemed to be living outside. There were dogs and babies and women cooking on deck wearing slit skirts. Smoke rose from frying pans on little stoves. I could see it all from the porthole.

Then there were the young boys bobbing about in the water, calling up to the big ship from between the boats, calling for money. That was when we were allowed to throw it in, it was for them. It was like a show, a performance, but they had to work for it. We couldn't just give it to them, we had to throw it. If you threw too much at a time, they'd have to dive so deep and stay under so long. They were like little darting brown fish. The coins would flash in the air and sparkle like the water on their backs. They'd wave and be grateful. It felt funny. It felt like a trick. It felt powerful in a bad way.

This port was really crowded. There were people everywhere, all close together. It was hot and sticky and I saw brown shiny skin and coolie hats.

We got into a rickshaw.

The man had his eyes down, and he didn't look at us as we piled in. We were four and he was one and he was going to pull us. He had no shoes. I didn't like it, but I knew I mustn't say anything. I thought, English people don't say anything. For a while it was all right. I wondered though how he was managing to pull us so fast and so easily. He was a small man, but I supposed he must be very strong. He was thin and I could see his muscles. But then we started to go more slowly.

The road was rising. All I could see was his back. It was like all the suffering in the world was in his back. I wanted to see his face. I wanted to see if it was angry or in pain. He was having to pull us up the hill as if he were an animal – as if it didn't matter to us that he couldn't manage it. It didn't matter that his chest was going to explode whilst we just sat there looking at the scenery.

I wanted to help. Not because I was kind but because it wasn't fair. I felt I was being torn in two as he got slower and slower and we just sat there. I wanted to rock the rickshaw – I wanted to get out. That would have been better than nothing.

I must have said something though.

'Don't worry, they're used to it,' they said.

Then at that moment I was ashamed.

We went up in the cable car – up to the Peak. Here all was space and light. Discreet footfalls of the people who bring easy living. No frying pans here, no swirling foreign people. The trouble was I liked both. Soon, one of those people behind closed doors would bring me Coca-Cola on a tray and perhaps we'd have ice-cream for lunch.

Then I was back in the kitchen and found myself slowly pouring Coca-Cola down the sink, seething about dirty money and mud.

I kept thinking about soldiers – all the soldiers – all the dead soldiers stretching back and back through time. I remember walking among the graves near the common and saying to the stones:

'If I was where you are, I'd have taken every one of you to my bed, because you're soldiers and you're too young to be lying here, and there are too many of you.'

I remembered my husband telling me about a battle. The soldiers had been ordered to walk across no man's land. They were under orders to walk into the bullets. They weren't allowed to take death on the run.

Higher and higher – further and further.

I went walking once in Richmond Park to King Henry's Mount – to the spot where he is said to have looked across to the place where they killed Anne Boleyn. When he saw the smoke he knew she was dead. Then he could gallop off to Jane Seymour. I remember thinking, She'd have given you a healthy son if you'd given her a chance. Why couldn't you wait a minute? Why couldn't you give her a chance?

'It's not fair,' I told the cameras.

The cameras were wherever I wanted them to be now.

It was so early in the morning. I bounced in to my husband.

'I'm going to see the dawn,' I said. 'Why don't you come?'

Silence. I got cross then.

'Why won't you come? It'll be wonderful.'

'I think I'll pass,' he said.

There was a man up near the Soldier Hospital on the hill – walking – a stranger. We smiled. As we were the only two people in the park it seemed the natural thing to do. I can't remember much more except that I picked up every scrap of litter in a little park on the way home and kept a scrap of coloured paper. I thought the Stranger had put it there for me. It was a coloured picture of a bird's feather. I felt as if I had an engine in my head and I couldn't turn it off.

I can't remember – all the cooking and shopping had to be done, but I can't remember doing it. I remember being light-headed with tiredness and joy and there being no time – or rather what time there was sped by at the speed of light.

8

The play set off on tour to four cities.

The hotel in the first city was lovely, set in dazzling grounds. I arrived, carried all my bags in and waited. No one looked up from behind the desk. Perhaps in real time this lasted only a second, but then it seemed a long time.

Can't she even smile? Can't she even look up and smile? I thought. She knows I'm here and I can see she's busy, but why can't she notice me and smile? I'll stand here for as long as she wants me to if she does that.

So I went and read a magazine. I read for about half an hour. The receptionists kept looking at me strangely. Eventually when I felt like it I wandered up and talked to them. They were quite civil.

This was to get worse.

At Seaside-by-the-Sea, when the same thing happened again, I just sat for a long time with my head down. The man at the desk came over after a while and shook me gently, saying my name – I made him wait a long time before I went to sign the book.

I didn't think the Stranger could see me at reception, but I knew he'd know which room I'd be given. I don't know – I think I thought I was allowed to be sad and tired in places where there were no cameras. I knew he'd hidden one in my hotel bedroom but I thought I'd have a few minutes to myself. So I found some stairs leading God knows where and went and hid for about half an hour. I remember feeling so guilty and faintly gratified at the Stranger's relief when I returned to where I was supposed to be.

The actor wanted to change hotels. Did I want to? It was unthinkable. I had to stay where the cameras were.

I often wash woollies when I stay in hotels. The rooms are warm and there are plenty of places to dry them. So I washed a lengthy blue shawl affair. I heard the Stranger say, as I lifted the heavy dripping mass from the bath – I heard him whisper:

'How are you going to dry it? Eh?'

'Oh, shut up,' I said. 'I'll show you.'

I rolled up the wet washing in several hotel bath-towels and then jumped all over them.

'See!' I said. 'Bone dry. Well, sort of. I bet you'd never have thought of that. You may be very important, and very clever – but you'd never have thought of that.'

I can't explain it but I felt I had a guardian angel. I felt he was really really there. He was with me all the time.

I got to Seaside-by-the-Sea in the dead of night. I was lawless when I got there. After ten hours on the motorway, I'd got lost and shot past it, past the turning. He was cross with me. He used to get cross when I was incompetent, but I told the camera that they'd done it on purpose – the road people. The sign was down beneath the road I was on and you couldn't see it until it was too late to turn off the motorway. I said I wasn't going to be defeated and headed for Scotland. He was so cross with me. I stopped at a little house near the motorway garage and some men told me how to turn round down a little road. I tried it but I ended up back at the garage. One of the men came with me in the end and I roared back south.

The Stranger said he wanted sex.

I used the rear-view mirror to put my lipstick on with one hand, the other on the wheel. I must have been doing about ninety.

'I've never seen that done before,' he said.

'You haven't seen anything yet,' I told him.

I then made love to an Everton mint. It's amazing what you can do to an Everton mint driving rather fast. It took hours. You can't crunch Everton mints – you have to wait till they get squishy and then you swallow the little bit that's left. I lit a cigarette then. The Stranger didn't approve of smoking, so I blew the smoke into his face – very gently.

There was a notice on the seafront at Seaside-by-the-Sea saying no one was to go on the beach at night – so I moved the rope and left the car where it said 'No Parking'. I took off my boots and socks – I wasn't mad enough to be completely impractical. There was a full moon and the tide was out a long way. The liquid sand was refreshing. Then I paddled in the shiny black water in the dark.

I went paddling in heaven.

I prayed to the whole world.

I said Our Father, even though I've always had a problem with 'Lead us not into temptation'. Why should our father lead us into temptation? It seems such a mean trick to play. However I said Our Father.

'Hail Mary, Hail Holy Queen,' I said. 'Shiva – Buddha – Adoni – Allah – Adoni – Allah – Tibet – Timor – Tibet – Timor – Tibet – Timor – Tiananmen – Tiananmen – Tiananmen – Lady in Burma – Lady in Burma – Lady in Burma – Vannunu – Vannunu – Vannunu. The men to do with Carl Bridgewater.'

I thought they could hear me.

The Stranger said he didn't like my nightie, my Victorian tent, so I bought another one. Sheer – long – white – decorous. It fitted better and it floated. I really liked this nightie.

The Stranger had been a soldier but now he was doing something else. He was fabulously wealthy because he'd written all the words – well, perhaps not all the words – of the songs on the radio. He did that in his spare time as light relief from his proper work. I was so proud of him because he was so good at what he did. I didn't want any of his boring money either. His money was so boring – even he found it boring.

I can't remember what tape was playing, probably my Soldiers of Song – my sultans of swing – who blow kisses through the bars of their rhymes. I was feeling so good. The room was pretty too, and the show had gone well. I'd washed my shawl, and my nightie really floated. The sky was clear. The air was clear too and the cedars were so blackly green. They were the only trees I could draw in art class at school.

I thought I'd go just a little bit higher.

I climbed out of the window. I was so, so high up. I sat there holding on – and then I leant forward. I heard the Stranger gasp. I knew he could see me – he was watching.

He was with friends though – I heard them gasp too. The sky seemed very near and the ground very, very far away.

This nightie is so demure, I thought. And so becoming. I've had a bath and I smell so nice. And my feet look so pretty in the moonlight. No one can make me come in until I'm ready. No one can make me do anything because there's nobody here.

I got bored then and cold, so I got down.

Sometimes the Stranger would make the tape jam if he didn't like the music. I'd change the tapes and only the one he wanted would go round. He seldom let me play *Born in the USA* – and never before a show. I wasn't to get hyped up. Sometimes I'd make him listen to my other music. He liked the Schubert, but he liked the Handel better, because it was quieter.

The Stranger didn't want me to use my car in the cities. He was most concerned about pollution – so I had to walk everywhere. I got so angry in the City in the West that I sat down in the middle of the road. I just walked into the middle of the road and sat down and held up the traffic.

My make-up bag hadn't been sent up from London. It wasn't at the theatre. They said they'd put it on a train and that it would arrive in time, but I didn't believe them. I tried to calm down. I felt panicky. Something would happen. The bag wouldn't arrive in time. My performance was in that bag – and so was my face. What would I do without them?

I tried to phone the man with the deep voice. Answerphone. I was so restless, so much walking. I was so tired.

I wanted to build my dressing-room nest. If I can only

just put all my things out. My lipstick and tablecloth and hairpins and everything, all nice and neat – I'll be all right. I have to make it my room NOW. I can't wait, I can't wait. Everything felt strange. I didn't know where to go. I had no room because my things weren't in it. I felt as though there were little birds in my throat and my heart was beating. I walked out of the stage door and sat down in the middle of the road for about five minutes and held up a bus full of people.

The driver got out and spoke to me.

'What are you doing?' he said.

'I have waited for ever at the sides of a million roads,' I said. 'I stand there patiently and I can never get across. I'm fed up. The cars can bloody well wait for me for a change.'

'I'm not a car,' he said. 'I'm a bus.'

'I can't help that,' I said.

Then Dee, who dressed my wig, came out of the stage door and sat down calmly beside me.

'You're very angry, aren't you?' she said quietly.

I nodded and then I got up because when people were kind it made me cry and I didn't want to.

Then the police arrived. I was extremely rude to a very young policeman. I must have said 'fuck' about fifteen times.

'What harm have I done?' I kept yelling. 'I haven't hurt anybody. I haven't done anything. While we're at it – what the fuck's happened to the City in the West? The streets have turned into fucking motorways!'

He ticked me off then for swearing.

'Oh bollocks,' I shouted. 'You lot are always swearing in the canteen and everywhere else.'

He was backing out the door.

'You're a horrible woman,' he said.

'You're absolutely right!' I shouted. 'We can be just as horrible as men!'

9

All my life I've envied people who have seen things on drugs. Aldous Huxley screaming with laughter at the absurdity of American cars. My husband telling me about looking into the eyes of a dog – on Hampstead Heath – very early in the morning after a party. He said it was like looking into limitless liquid goodness. An actor I knew said he'd seen evolution. He'd looked into the clear water of a stream to the pebbles beneath and said he'd seen tiny little dinosaurs coming out of the stones. Tiny little dinosaurs – I envied that, but then there's the poor Crazy Diamond (Shine On). But I'd be all right and I was like them – I'd seen golden lights that lit up the sky.

The Stranger was telling me to change the world – to smash all the big supermarkets and give the small shops a chance. So I bought their things and put them in the kitchen window for the cameras to see.

I was tripping cold turkey. Perhaps I was drugged by life – but by the dark as well as the light.

I shut him out. The only person who's ever really loved me – twenty years now. He kept trying to bring me down from the high.

'You'll crack up,' he said. 'I can't pick up the pieces.'

I kept screaming at him.

'You want me to crack up! You want me to crack up but I'm still standing! I'm still standing. I'm all right! I'm ALL RIGHT!'

I didn't want to talk to him – I wanted to talk to the Stranger. We'd chat. He told me what to put in my suitcase to take on tour.

'Take that jacket,' he said. 'And you'll need a posh frock.'

At Seaside-by-the-Sea I met a civil servant. I sat next to him and we dined together. Functions can be very heavy going. I get so bored talking about myself and my job – it drives me to distraction – so it's hardly fair to expect the person next to me to talk about himself and what he does. But this time it was wonderful. He was a kind man, gentle and calm.

'England is the only country in Europe that doesn't know how much money it has,' he said.

Apparently someone hadn't understood the computer – or had programmed it wrongly or something. It was his job to find out how much there was in the kitty. It was going to take him four years to sort it out.

Did I dream that?

Then he told me something even better. He told me about the blue flame. He told me that the blue in a flame was very cold – something to do with another form of energy, not nuclear. That energy need not necessarily come from heat. It could come from cold. I loved that. Cold heat – hot snow.

I love people telling me things I'd never thought of asking about. I thought the Stranger would be interested too. He was with me as I ate and drank and he liked the man. He was pleased with me. He'd said I should go out and talk to people and not live in the half-dark with the music and the picnics in candle-light.

Some of the company had a photo-call one afternoon with some transvestites. I never know quite how to behave with transvestites. I don't know why – I just don't. I don't know where I am. I get confused. I don't know whether I'm talking to a man or a woman.

We went to their club after our curtain came down and they were marvellous – sexy and camp. But then one of them started singing a song about my husband – despising him – sneering at him. I left before she or he had finished singing.

I went through the doors and started walking back along the seafront. The water was all oily and black, but then my feet wouldn't stop. I didn't know they weren't going to stop – my feet just kept walking. On and on – past the hotel – on and on. It was late. I was frightened.

I came to a high wire fence. I climbed it, went down the other side and got into a skip. I rearranged all the rubble and found a plank of wood. I lay down on that, with a stone for a pillow. It was quite comfortable. I can pretend to be homeless, I thought, then I'll know what it feels like. I must have lain there for half an hour and then I heard voices. I remember thinking the Stranger had sent someone to make sure I was all right. He'd been whispering to me – over and over again:

'That's enough now. That's enough.'

'I'm OK,' I called out. 'I'm OK.'

'Bloody hell! You gave us a fright.'

It was the builders. It can't have been the builders. It was the middle of the night. Perhaps it was the police. I can't remember. I can't remember whether I climbed the fence or whether they opened the gate or whether there was a gate.

'I thought I'd pretend to be homeless,' I said.

Whoever they were they didn't bat an eyelid.

It was as if I were being pulled by strings.

I had to do as I was told.

I stood for half an hour at the traffic lights. The drivers would stare at me as I waited for the lights to change – red – green – red – green. Some of them would wait for me on their green, but I didn't move. Some looked puzzled, some looked impatient. I wanted to be cold. I wanted to know how it felt to be really cold before I went back to my warm and pretty room.

'Are you all right?' some of the walkers would ask.

But then the lights would change and they'd cross over.

In the city, a city in the West, there was a cathedral. I was to go there. I kept getting lost. Before I set out I was to stick a safety pin into my hand. Then I had to put my hand into the pocket of my jeans so that no one could see. The Stranger didn't want anyone to see the pin. But with every step it hurt. It hurt as I moved.

I kept asking the way, and eventually I got there. There was a 'Gift Shoppe' as you went in. I was incensed. How could they want the first impression to be of buying and selling? Couldn't they put the shop somewhere else? At the side or the back?

Someone working in the shop asked for my autograph, but I didn't want to talk to her. I wanted to be peaceful and read the writing on the stones from hundreds of years before. I didn't want to look at tea-towels.

Jesus had always been real to me. He really did die. The nuns in Japan said that we little girls had helped hammer in the nails.

'Everyone in the world who has ever lived', they said, 'has played a part in the nail-hammering, and you are no exception.'

We looked up to the nuns even though they made us feel wicked. We had to call them 'madam'. It was a Catholic convent, a French order, and they were mostly Irish nuns. I started at five and stayed until it was time for English boarding school.

I didn't think I would make it to heaven because I wasn't Catholic. It was upsetting but inevitable because only Catholics went there. Laura Potts wasn't Catholic either, but she wasn't having any of it.

'I'm Scottish,' she said. 'And I'm going to heaven.'

I thought she was very brave.

Jesus was the one person I could never have imagined. All the terrible things that happened to him were partly my fault. They must have been my fault because Madam said so. We spent so much time thinking about all the terribleness when we made the Stations of the Cross. We used to go slowly round the chapel gazing up at the nails, and the prickly crown, and think about the blood coming out of his side. We used to look at his feet crossed over and skewered.

They must have had an extra-long special nail for his feet, I thought, so that it would reach through to the wood. They must have hammered so hard and for such a long time to split the feet bones. With the hands it would have been quicker, but not the feet. And why didn't the hand nails rip through the skin? Poor Jesus, he might have fallen off.

The more you felt the horror, the holier you must be.

I liked the holy feeling. With Jesus it was dark, but the particular blue of the Virgin Mary's mantle was very becoming, and she made me feel holy in a lighter way. In any event she had second billing on the altar – the one in my bedroom.

My dad wouldn't genuflect when he came in, which I thought was very mean of him. But when he caught me smoking once, all he did was grin – I think he was pissed from the cocktail party going on downstairs. Still, it was cosy in my room – altar nice and tidy, tucked up with a Coke, candles lit, American biscuits from the PX and Enid Blyton.

Now with Enid Blyton you knew where you were. Just like Jesus. There were good people and bad people, and my money was on the good people. I wanted to be with them. But the trouble was I wasn't good enough to go to heaven because I wasn't a Catholic. The best thing to do would be to get so holy that I could change into one later. So I'd do sacrifices.

Being humble was tricky. Even though I could get myself into a very humble frame of mind and concentrate on being lowly, as soon as I felt pleased about how lowly and humble I was I'd be committing the sin of pride. So I was scuppered. A no-win situation.

Still, there was always pain. After a laborious quarter-hour of prayers, I'd lie flat on my back with my head up and see how long I could stand it.

It was confusing that the madams seemed to imply that sex and babies were somehow unnatural. Not that I knew what sex was – none of us did. I thought you prayed and prayed like barren Sarah in the Bible, who, even though she was forty, suddenly conceived a child.

'Oh, your poor mothers,' the madams would say. 'They are such wonderful brave women.'

They made me think then that you had to go through something truly terrible to have a baby.

Yet we loved these madams. We were afraid of them but they were all mixed up with the Virgin Mary and Jesus, so they were all part of the mysterious holy love.

I managed to sit still for a while in the cathedral. It was so cool. Then I had to make it back for the show. I was so tired but I had to keep going – on and on. Working – dancing – walking – praying for the world. I'd get so angry with the Stranger sometimes because of all the feeling.

'Find yourself another fucking saint!' I'd say. 'You're so mean to me to make me feel so much. So mean.'

I was burning up – on fire – burning out.

'You'll lose your daughter,' he whispered to me one day.

I'd wanted her to come to the city, and then we'd drive home together the next morning. She arrived at the theatre. She looked at me strangely – guardedly. She said she had to go back after the matinée because she was babysitting that night. I wouldn't let her go.

'You're staying and that's that!'

We had a row about money and cashpoints.

'Mum, you're different,' she said. 'You keep shouting.'

Later I found out that the director had taken her aside and told her I was tired and needed a rest. She'd come into my dressing room, calm and kind as usual. She knew my daughter because the latter had watched the dress rehearsal back in London. I couldn't believe what I was hearing. She wanted me to take a week off from the tour to rest.

'Why?' I asked.

'Because you're very tired,' she said.

'No I'm not,' I shot back. 'Besides I've got a contract. I can't just not do my job.'

She kept insisting.

'Is it my work?' I asked.

'No,' she said. 'Your work's fine.'

'Well, I'm staying then. If the boss wants me to go – then I'll go. Otherwise I'm staying.'

I dare not remember much more about that day. We'd been watching television in the hotel bedroom – a racing car had spun over and burst into flames – but the driver was all right. My daughter hadn't reacted.

'Don't you care!' I screamed. 'Don't you care that he's all right?'

Her eyes were so strange. She looked so afraid. My husband was to tell me later when I asked him.

'Why on earth did you let her come?'

'She thought she could save you.'

We went shopping that Saturday. I bought so many silly things – we could hardly carry it all. I bought a black rooster made of some kind of black metal. I couldn't stop buying strange things. I was so short with her. She seemed so unhappy and she wouldn't tell me why. She stayed with me during the two shows, but went into wardrobe for company when I was on-stage.

I didn't sleep very much that Saturday night. I had to keep keeping myself in the boring world. It felt strange to try to sleep in silence. I'd got used to dozing to music.

We packed and left – but not before we'd had a fearsome row about cold toast. Then we argued about which way the road sign meant. It was horrible. We fought all the way. She turned the radio off without asking. I was livid with rage. As we neared London I got so lost. We had travelled eighty miles and we were now on cone-laden dual carriageways. None of the signs meant anything. Eventually I had to get out and pee on a little green – in full view of passing traffic. I had no choice but she must have died of embarrassment.

Eventually, eventually, across the way I saw a tiny little sign. A very old white and black, or rather black and white, road sign. It said 'Hampstead'. We live nowhere near Hampstead but at least I knew where it was so we went there.

Once in 1971 I saw a woman just off the Edgware Road standing by her car, sobbing. I got out.

'What's the matter?'

'I can't find the M1.'

'I'm working at Nottingham rep, just follow me,' I said. 'The Edgware Road turns into the M1. It's a breeze.'

I found Hampstead and then we were home. My daughter went into the house.

She talked to her father. I knew she had to talk to her father. I didn't know I was going to stay in the car, but I just stayed and stayed – staring. My husband came out.

'Aren't you coming in?'

'No.'

Then I did go in. I stood there. He came to put his arms around me.

He's stopping me, I thought. He's stopping me.

I started fighting him.

I can run away very fast because my case is packed, I thought. I can run away now.

I darted into the conservatory to snatch up a carton of cigarettes and ran for the car.

I'll have to get food, I thought. But I can do it. I'll be all right once I get going. I'm a bit tired, but I'll be all right. Food – I must have food – food and petrol. But I've got to drive north and I'm tired.

It felt good to drive off with the music nice and loud. The garage had sandwiches – it was my home garage, but they'd changed it, and now it had sandwiches and different men. Before they were Indian men – their Alsatian used to sleep in the office. It was all different and it had sandwiches and I had an ice-cream.

I drove another 150 miles and got there. Well – it was impossible really to get there, because, however many times I tried to approach the hotel, the one-way street seemed to be going the wrong way. It was Sunday and there were no coppers about. A very nice man had explained how to get to the hotel. I'd offered him money to come with me in the car and show me but he said no – and anyway he had enough money, he didn't want any more. So I went the wrong way down the street and nobody saw.

I didn't like the first room they gave me at the hotel. I

couldn't see out. I knew the Stranger didn't like the room either, and wouldn't have put the cameras in a room like that. They gave me another one right at the very top. There was a lovely four-poster but the window was small and it had spikes at the sill. I knew then that the cameras were there because he didn't want me to sit in any more windows – and that was why he'd chosen a room with spikes.

In hotels I always had to know where the fire escape was – I had to be able to get out – and this time there really were cameras, real cameras.

I wouldn't use the lift. I thought it would crash down through all the floors and kill me – so it had to be the back stairs. They were concrete and one of the hotel people frowned at me when I met her there. I lost count sometimes of how many floors I'd climbed. The strangest thing of all was that the paintings on the walls in the corridors would reproduce themselves every four or five paintings. The corridors twisted and turned, so you never knew where you were because you couldn't use the pictures as a guide.

The porter had said I wasn't to touch the fire-escape door.

'I just want to see if it opens,' I said.

He got cross then and left. He really was cross. I opened the door and stepped out. It slammed behind me.

Shit! I thought. He's gone away, there's no one to let me in. Oh well – there's bound to be a way out.

I stepped out into a courtyard with buildings in the distance. There were hundreds and hundreds of rubber bands on the ground – I picked them all up. Then I walked on, but there were always more rubber bands. This place was enclosed – the paths were paved. It was a vast housing estate and there were so many rubber bands. I put them all on my wrist.

Whichever way I turned I couldn't get out. I tried everywhere but I could not get out. Tall buildings and no one, no one there – no one walking. There was a window in a sort of shed which said, 'Break in Case of Fire', but I thought I'd better not.

Then I found a secret garden right in the middle of this concrete courtyard. Someone must have made a secret garden, but what was odd was that everything seemed to be in bloom at the same time. I looked at all the flowers in this strange place of stone walkways and no people, and chatted to the Stranger.

'I know you don't like gardening,' I said.

I walked about a bit more – quite calmly. I knew I couldn't get out, but I had a lot of rubber bands.

Whenever I was incompetent, I blamed the Stranger. I told him he was so mean to do this.

I saw buildings far away but there were no roads leading to them. I didn't panic in any way, but I couldn't seem to solve this problem of the buildings and no roads.

Then I saw some plastic sheeting, reasonably clean, in amongst some broken bricks the builders had left. So I flapped it about a bit, lay down and tried to go to sleep.

I used to write to the Stranger asking, 'Are you all right?' I'd stopped sending the letters to where I thought he was. I sent them care of a DJ on the radio.

Where are my letters now? Where did they go?

Then there were the men.

'We saw you on our cameras,' they said. 'Do you want to come back with us?'

I went with them down to their office in the basement. There were so many screens – wallfuls of them – relaying pictures from the cameras all over the estate. They didn't ask me any questions at all.

'We've been watching you,' they just said.

I stayed awhile. They let me use their loo. I think they knew who I was – but I'm not sure. They were very gentle.

'What do you see on there?' I asked them – as the shots flicked from doorways to walkways.

'Fighting,' they answered.

Then they told me where the exit was, but I still couldn't get out. They'd come part of the way, but I had to ask another man where the door was. He wasn't so nice. He looked at me as if I was nuts when I suggested all the corridor walls would make great art galleries. But out of ten thousand people on the estate there must have been one painter.

I remember nothing about the rest of the day until that evening.

In this city, at this theatre, I'd been warned about a man who collected autographs, but would I mind meeting him. The trouble was he was sick. He'd lunge at people and try to grope them – poor man.

He's got a problem, I thought.

But it was fine. He had a strange, eager sort of look and there was a woman with him taking care of him. I signed the book.

Then I ordered a cab. I just couldn't walk any more. It arrived and I got in. The driver's face terrified me. He turned round and smiled, but not with his eyes, just with his mouth and his teeth were dirty.

'I'll take care of you,' he said. 'Where are we going?'

'I want another car! I want another car!'

I heard my voice – high-pitched. I got out and went back through the stage door. Seconds later the minicab firm rang back.

'What's wrong? Do you want to make a complaint?'

'No, no, nothing is wrong!'

I could hardly say that I didn't like the man's face and that he frightened the shit out of me.

10

I threw my wedding ring away.

Then I threw away my little yellow diamond – the one my mum-in-law gave me. Her husband gave it to her, and she gave it to me. I loved that ring, it was so delicate and so graceful, but I threw it away.

Why?

First I'd dropped them both into the waste-paper basket, but then I heard the Stranger's voice.

'That's not good enough,' he said.

So I fished them out of the basket, opened the window, and hurled them as far as I could across the hotel car park.

Then I threw away my husband's ski jacket. It was black with a blue collar. He's a generous man and, after years of borrowing, he'd let me have it. I loved it because I felt safe in it. It was warm and it had an inside pocket so I never lost my keys. I love inside pockets – only men get inside pockets.

I didn't want to do any of this, but I had to – I couldn't stop it. I felt I'd be taken away if I disobeyed the radio people and the Stranger. So I stuffed the jacket into a litter bin outside the hotel.

Then I made my own wedding ring.

I made it from thread wound round and round my finger. The end neatly tucked in and secured with a pin. I could hide it on stage underneath my prop ring, but then my finger got infected because the thread never really dried.

The ring I wore in the play was the Stranger's ring too. It was a blue stone with markings attached to a plain gold band. If I looked at it sideways they were his initials. It broke on the last performance of the tour – the stone part fell off on to my dressing table. I was shaken, I thought it was a bad omen. But now I had a wedding ring and a talisman – so it was all right. I had to wait though to wear it, until the soreness from the damp thread had healed.

The Stranger would tease me so.

'I'll knock on your door in half an hour,' I used to hear him say.

Once in the City in the North, I saw his breakfast tray outside the room next to mine. Sometimes I heard his laughter, but it wasn't my place to disturb him – so I never did.

I told him once that I knew him. I knew he had to go where there was space. I told him I knew what he did when he couldn't bear it. I knew he took out his little sailboat and was all by himself on the open sea. I said I wasn't like him – I had to go somewhere very small where I'd feel safe.

Then the company went on a boat trip and I had to too, because the Stranger liked boats, and I might even meet him if I did as I was told.

I left my room and rushed down the stairs. The river

was alongside the hotel. I was running along the bank. I could see all the actors and stage management and crew were already on the boat.

'You're late! You're late!' they yelled.

'No I'm not!' I shouted back. 'I've got one minute left and I'll make it.'

I ran up and over the little bridge and leapt on to the boat.

They'd organized food and drink and it was fun.

Why do you hide away? I thought. Being out is better – being with them is better – they're nice.

Then I knew why I hid. They could all read my thoughts, every one of them. They'd laugh knowingly because of something I was thinking.

Oh, Christ! I thought. I'll have to control my thinking now. I'm so ashamed.

So I'd go round the boat, looking at everyone in turn – making myself think really nice things about them.

They'll pick it all up and not be offended, I thought.

Then I got to my understudy and I couldn't help it. To be fair, I thought.

You don't like me, do you?

No. I don't. Was what I thought she thought.

Well, fuck you then! I thought.

And all the while the riverbank and the reeds and a man at the wheel telling us about ducks and coots and wonderful strange birds that he knew the names of. He told us ancient history of the city on the river with a microphone. I wanted to go back to my room then, where I could think in peace. My head hurt from trying to keep my thoughts from thinking themselves, and from people reading my mind.

We stopped for a drink. We all got off the boat. The sun

was out. The river water licked the muddy bank. The blades of grass were so fat and green and pointed. The sun poured growing gold and the roots sucked and drank. The umbrellas waved hello and the tables and chairs said:

'Siddown, siddown. Have a drink. Have a sprawl. Have a loll. Have a smoke, crack a joke. Let's immobilize the mobiles – chuck 'em in the river. Let's fuck about, the sun's out. Let's spend money. We'll melt together and turn our feet in the heat.'

Perhaps I wanted to die with the beauty of it all. I was so sure the Stranger would be waiting for me in the pub – but he wasn't.

I was so disappointed. I really thought I'd meet him that time. I never considered hopelessness, because I knew that he decided everything, and I mustn't cross him or he'd be very angry with me.

When I was little, I liked going too high on the swing – especially wearing the medieval headdress my mum made me. It was long and pointed – like a witch's hat without the brim – with a long chiffon veil streaming out in the wind from the pointed top. I liked swinging too high. You had to start off standing – to pick up speed – and then you'd sit. I liked the jerk as the chain swung back. One day I thought I wouldn't put my hands on the chains – I'd put them very low down on the seat. I wondered if I could stay on while the seat wobbled. I fell off. I remember the bang on my chest as I hit the ground still wearing my medieval hat.

I remembered the swing when I tried the same thing on the fire-escape railing. I held on low down and wobbled a bit. The corner of the metal stairway jutted right out into mid-air so you could see everywhere and right down through it as well. Fathoms down through the little holes in the iron. I balanced myself on the rail. It was a good rush looking below but, too stoned, I got off. I didn't want to die.

Being ten and climbing trees to the top taught me something else. There was a boy – Daniel Brook – I remember his tears so vividly. He couldn't make it to the top. It was so easy to climb when you knew no fear – but he did, he was frightened. I was a girl, I had a choice. I could be brave or I could be helpless. He had no choice. His mother was looking up – her face all confused. Cross he wasn't brave, but wanting to protect him. I knew that you didn't beat a boy – even if you could, you just didn't.

That night I set fire to the furniture. Well, not set fire to, but melted the varnish on the bedside table.

'You are a fire hazard,' the hotel people told me.

They didn't like the chiffon scarves I'd draped over the lights, and they didn't like me having candles. They came in a sort of posse. But the point was they need never have known. I was tidying up my room myself each day. I could just as easily have hidden it, the scorched bit, with an ashtray. But I telephoned down and told them what had happened and said I'd buy the furniture. They then asked me not to light candles any more.

'You better confiscate them then,' I said. 'I'm not to be trusted.'

I gave the scorched bedside table to the Portuguese girl who cleans my house for me. They'd been living in one room, the three of them, but now they'd found a flat. She told me how clever her husband was – he'd revarnish it. I kept the other one. I still have it – it's in the spare room.

I'm not afraid of a table. The hotel made me buy two and charged me five hundred pounds.

At Seaside-by-the-Sea I got so tired using the stairs all the time. The Stranger didn't want me to waste electricity using the lift – so it had to be the stairs. I climbed them to the top. I pushed the door open and I was on the roof. There were little pebbles on the concrete and no railings. You could see for miles. I went to the edge and looked out to sea.

Then an old man came through the door and was perfectly pleasant. It was just that I wasn't allowed up there. We chatted about this and that.

'What a fabulous place this roof is,' I said. 'Why don't you have a café up here with tables and chairs?'

At Seaside-by-the-Sea there was a tower.

We were all invited to go up one morning – all the company. It was out of season. I wanted to go even though I knew I was being filmed all the time. By this time the cameras were anywhere and everywhere. I waited and waited but none of my friends came.

The man who worked there took me up. He pointed out the nuclear power station. It was warm for the time of year and there were people paddling.

'Do you ever swim here?' I asked him, because the Stranger wanted to know.

'You must be joking.' He laughed. 'Put your arm in there and it glows when it comes out.'

'Shouldn't someone tell all the people in the sea about that?' I asked.

He shrugged – or perhaps he said something. I can't remember.

I got to the theatre that night.

'Where the hell were you?' I asked. 'I was there for ages.'

I'd been waiting at the wrong entrance.

We did the performance as usual, and at the end of the play, when everyone was torn and bleeding and dirty and before the music started, the skylight shattered as it always did. All the sugar glass came crashing down – some pieces quite heavy, and everything fell at great speed.

I'd been worrying about this. Someone was trying to kill us. I kept pulling everyone out of the way.

The next day I went shopping. I went into Woolworth's and there were so many tapes and CDs. The same phrase went round and round in my head:

The Soldiers of Song. The Soldiers of Song.

I thought the 'Soldiers of Song' could change the world. But I didn't know any of the new soldiers. So I read out their names in the store. I whispered them into my ear microphone. I told the Stranger that I wasn't going to get stuck in my time – the sixties.

The following morning he made me get up so very early. I was to drive somewhere. I didn't know where – but he'd show me. I left the city as the sun was coming up. There was a signpost – to the left was the town where my husband had lived twenty years ago with his first wife; I turned to the right. I drove on. I knew the Stranger would tell me where to go and he did. Down another road was the abbey – the gates were open. There was no one to pay and there was no one, absolutely no one about.

I could play my music so loud and the blackbird was waiting for me as I turned the key in the lock of the car.

I walked up a hill. To my left was a field of horses and I stopped. They all came over from the far side of the field. I didn't have anything for them, but they still took it in turns to butt me with their heads. All except one. She stayed far, far away. She wouldn't even look at me. She was Mrs Thatcher.

Then I walked and walked. I had my wellingtons on, but the grass was long and soon my boots were full of water. Then I met a jogger and we talked about running.

'As you get older,' he said, 'you can't run as fast, but you can run further and longer.'

Then I saw the peacock strutting about in front of Poet's Abbey. I thought he was Michael Heseltine.

'Can I touch your tail?' I asked him.

He flicked it and walked away.

I drove back glazed through the rush hour.

All these people are going to work and they've slept, I thought. Why can't I sleep?

'You don't need sleep,' came the reply.

I washed my wet socks in the hotel and ordered breakfast. Then I went out and bought food for my lunchtime and night-time picnics. I had to buy wine from all the countries in the world for the cameras to see.

'Where's the English wine?' I demanded.

They were rather apologetic.

I couldn't carry it all. I had to get a taxi, I just couldn't carry it all. I got in – the driver was Indian.

'Tell me about India.'

'What now?'

That night I got lost backstage. They were all old theatres and this one was full of twisting corridors. I hadn't explored it properly and in the second act I had to come on stage left. I went under the stage – down the steps – I followed the arrows – but each time I ended up in the same place – in the wings, stage right.

'I'm going to be off! Christ, I'm going to be off.'

I was running then – running. Alice found me.

'I can't find the stage! I can't find the stage!'

She knew where it was. She showed me.

I was making mistakes. I couldn't remember whether I'd done an entrance or not. One of the actors would always have a glass of water for me at a certain point – and he was worried when he looked at me. I played funny hiding games with the cue light – the light in the wings used by all of us.

I moved it so the Stranger couldn't see me. I left it to the last minute to go on when I heard my line. I was angry with him – angry having to do as he asked.

'Why are you so mean to me? So mean!'

I was tired – stupefied with tiredness. My head was full of scratchy cotton wool. I was giving up. I was losing everything – and I wanted to give him up, but I couldn't. I couldn't give the Stranger up.

If I could just have a break from feeling so much.

'I'll live by myself,' I muttered in the wings. 'I'll get a cat and live in a flat.'

My oldest girlfriend came to see a matinée. I kept her waiting for a long time. I never keep people waiting. The Stranger liked to watch me wash off the blood in the shower, and the water was so warm and strong on my skin.

I stayed a long time in the shower, even though I knew she was waiting.

11

Then one morning I looked down from the spiky window to the street below and I saw the Stranger.

I saw him carrying a child. He was so big and the child so small. It seemed the baby was in a boat. The Stranger's arms were like a boat.

Then I saw my husband and his friend. They looked furtive. They were using cash cards at the bank.

I saw them.

They looked so ill at ease.

They're stealing my money, I thought. They're stealing my money!

'You'll have to leave England,' the Stranger said.

I was driving round the park. It was looking so beautiful. There were tears pouring down my face.

'No,' he said. 'You have to give it all up. Everything. Your family – your home – your work – everything. You have to leave everything and go to Colorado to have a baby.'

'I'm too old,' I said.

'No, it'll be all right. You have to go to America and have a baby who will grow up to save the world.'

'What must I do?' I asked him. 'What must I do?'

'Let it be,' said the car radio.

Tears streaming down my face. I could control neither them nor my life. I had to take orders from the Stranger and the men on the radio.

My husband had gone away for a few days. He'd gone to Antwerp. Then the radio whispered, 'Antwerp', late one night when I got back from the theatre.

'I know,' I told it. 'I know.'

'He's having an affair,' said the man on the radio.

'It isn't true. It isn't true.'

Then everything slotted into place. He'd never left her. He'd never left his first wife. She lived a mile away. He saw her all the time. The radio even told me the name of the street where she still lived – near us.

Sometimes he went to see her in the dead of night. That was why he was cross with me when I played my music in the kitchen in the early hours – he couldn't steal out into the night and see her. There was a motor cycle in the garage next door. That was how he could get there quickly. She hadn't remarried at all – it was a lie – she was still married to him. He was taking our money and giving it to her. The radio voice said:

'You paid for her new kitchen. And what about her son?'

My husband had another child. My daughter had a half-brother.

One night I put a wooden chair on the edge of the rostrum in the wings – during the play. I rocked on it back and forth – back and forth. It was getting nearer and nearer the edge all the time. The stage manager was watching me.

'Be careful,' she said. 'Be careful!'

She left the book and walked towards me.

'Don't you fucking touch me,' I whispered. 'I'll be all right. The Stranger will catch me.'

The chair legs got nearer and nearer the edge and I fell backwards. I fell three or four feet, but I came to no harm. I was so relaxed as I fell. I never considered the other actors having to work through the noise I was making.

That was unlike me to spoil a piece of work.

After the second show I had my usual picnic late in my hotel room. Food spread on the carpet on a cloth. I kept dropping things and cleaning up meticulously. I'd clean up every crumb.

I kept offering people fruit cake. No one ever wanted any.

Who washed up at the Last Supper?

12

I came home in May from the tour and watched VE Day on the television with a cardigan over my head.

I thought the Queen could see me through our television camera.

'What are you doing?' my husband asked.

It boiled up into a furious row. There were razor blades between us – so I roared off in the car, with my music blaring, to look at the Houses of Parliament and the river.

When I came back he started shouting at me.

'They'll hear you,' I said. 'They'll hear us.'

'Who?'

'The house is bugged,' I said.

'But why would they bug you?'

'You mean, what I say isn't important enough?'

I was to turn on him – viciously – it was so ugly.

I kept saying to myself as I drove the car, 'I have friends in low places.' I was utterly convinced he was seeing his first wife. I thought he'd given me AIDS. I thought he was homosexual.

Then I thought the nastiest, ugliest thing of all.

'Nine times,' the Stranger whispered in my ear.

'What do you mean?' I asked.

'He's slept with your daughter nine times.'

That voice. I turned to ice.

Then I thought how my husband always called out before he went into her room:

'Are you decent?'

Then the light left on on the landing. Why? It wasn't so that she wouldn't trip over in the night – it was so that he himself could see.

I was at the end.

I was in my car. The radio was on but for some reason I was making myself do without the music. Someone was talking about ritual sacrifice. They were sacrificing a goat and then giving details of the slaughter. I could hear the animal screaming. I turned the car around – away from where I was going. The goat was dying. You could hear it squealing. It was my daughter. He was killing her.

I was spinning. My eyes prickling – itching with tiredness. I had to get to London – seventy, eighty miles an hour. I stopped at a garage.

'I need to use your phone. Now, now. Please – please! I'll pay. I'll pay!'

'I'm sorry but this is a private phone.'

'Please, oh please – just this once!'

'No. I'm sorry. It's company policy.'

'You'll pay for this!' I shouted. 'You'll be sorry. It's my daughter!'

'I'm sorry. You cannot use the phone.'

'I have to phone the police,' I screamed.

I tried another garage. The man who worked there let me use the phone in his office. He stayed there. I was shouting down the phone – but the police said I'd have to speak to the people in my area.

So I got back in the car and drove down the motorway at a hundred miles an hour for two hours. I kept my hand on the horn for most of the time. Sometimes the cars wouldn't get out of my way – especially the big ones. The big Fords and the Mercedes. They wouldn't move over even with the horn blaring.

'I don't care whether I live or die,' I muttered.

Then I drove right up close to their bumpers. I was inches away and they still didn't move. So I said in a level and controlled voice:

'I'm very, very tired and I'm not a very good driver.'

I knew my voice was being beamed into their cars and that they could hear me.

They moved then – they moved their big smug cars aside and let me through.

Oh Christ – sweet Jesus Christ – I can't slow down. The motorway is curving and I'm frightened. The wheel – the wheel. What do I do with the wheel? It doesn't like me – it doesn't like being held too tight. I'll skid – the car will slip away. I think I can hold it but it's pulling away – it's fighting me. I must hold on to the wheel – but the steel barrier is coming so close. We'll all die and there will be sparks – will it hurt? I don't want to kill anyone. Oh Christ – my head is fizzing and my heart is beating in my throat.

I got to our police station then and told them what was happening at home and they said they'd come.

They arrived. The two policewomen went into the sitting room with my daughter. I went into the garden, smoked a cigarette, did some deadheading.

They'll sort it out, I thought. I don't have to do anything any more. I'll get a cat. I'll get a little flat and a cat and I'll live by myself.

Then I came in, and overheard the police saying that because of the allegations they would have to go through with their normal procedures. With that they left.

Then the three of us found ourselves shouting at each other in the kitchen.

'If you love me, how can you be doing this to me!' screamed my daughter.

'I have to protect you from Daddy,' I insisted.

'How could you think such a terrible thing? Dad would never hurt me!'

'You're having an affair! That's the only explanation for all this mess!' he yelled at me.

'I've never even met him!' I screamed. 'And don't shout at me. Nobody shouts at me!'

I picked up his glass of Coke and threw it at him. He ducked. The glass smashed. The Coke ran down the wall. We went on shouting and yelling as I cleaned it all up.

I found the broken stem of the glass still in my hand. I walked towards him. My daughter glided past me and took the glass from my hand.

I tried to run away again then. I was trying to get out of the house to drive to the country to stay with my dad. He tried to stop me. He grabbed hold of me. His arm was round my neck. I bit his hand. He lost his grip. Then there were red sparks in my head and I couldn't stop myself trying to kick my way out of it.

Then he started to make a move – his fist raised. Our daughter put herself between us.

'No, Dad! Don't do it!'

'If you really think all this incest is going on,' he said, 'why are you abandoning her and going to the country?'

I ran up to my daughter's room. I had to find her flute – I hadn't seen it for months. I thought he'd sold it. I tipped out all the drawers and made a fearful mess. My daughter put her head round the door:

'If I ask you to stay – will you stay for me?'

'Yes.'

She kept saying, 'Daddy isn't having an affair.'

But it didn't make any difference.

She went to spend the evening with a friend. We were left face to face. I put the music on.

'If we have to listen to fucking music,' he said, 'put the Pavarotti on!'

I poured two glasses of wine.

'What did you do that for?' he asked. 'I don't want any wine – I'm drinking Coke.'

'It's for him.'

'Oh, my God,' he said. 'If I can convince you that you've imagined all this horror – would you still want us to split?'

'Yes.'

'But you don't even know him.'

'It doesn't matter,' I said. 'It doesn't make any difference.'

I changed the tape then and put on some rock music. I drank my wine, smoked my cigarettes and played tape after tape.

He sat there immobile.

Our daughter came in.

'You can hear it down the street,' she said. 'I thought there was a party going on.'

'Some party,' said my husband.

And then, I think it was the same night, I said to the only person who has loved me for so long – through the dark and the light I said:

'Oh, why don't you go,' I said. 'Why don't you go where it's warm. It's ice here. There's no love here.'

I remember his head in his hands and his tears.

I thought he was acting.

13

He got up to leave and I followed him into the hall.

And as he was walking down the street I went down the path a little way and shrieked:

'Aren't you going to say *au revoir* to your daughter?'

He turned.

'I've already said goodbye,' he said.

I looked up. My daughter was waving him goodbye from the window.

'I am innocent of all charges,' he said. 'I am an innocent man.'

I didn't watch him walk away.

It was all wrong. It wasn't right. It wasn't true. The only thing that was true was that my brain was nearly broken. I was to stay on fire for four more days.

The strange thing was that I did the performance on the Wednesday and I went to a lunch do at the theatre before it and I functioned. It seemed to go on and on – the people standing up making speeches. I couldn't concentrate on what they were saying. Not only that, the cameras were in the foyer, and not only could they see me and hear me – they knew my thoughts.

When it was over I went to my dressing room. I was having to share it by now – another play had joined the repertoire. It wasn't so much that they'd touched my things, but someone had taken down some newspaper cuttings I'd stuck on the locker so that the corridor camera could see.

'They have no right,' I muttered. 'They have no right. I wanted those cuttings there.'

I ripped all my cards away from the mirror and threw them in the drawer. If the room couldn't be mine alone I wanted to have nothing – no room.

I went missing in the interval and I had no idea of the time. No one knew where I was. Alice found me eventually, just before curtain-up. I don't know who I was talking to – but I had to go to a huge rehearsal room to talk to the cameras. I did the second act.

I have absolutely no recollection of driving myself home. All I know is the phone was ringing and ringing. I picked it up.

'Well, hello there,' I said.

'My agent's got me a criminal lawyer,' said my husband.

'Too right,' I said.

'Listen, our daughter's going through a really tough time. She's got her exams this week and I've talked to her. She says she can't concentrate. She told me you've turned some of the posters to the wall.'

'Only the ones you bought.'

The point was, I liked the Caillebotte. A man and a woman, her arm through his, walking down a street in Paris. They looked so easy together. It depressed me.

What was becoming odder and odder was the more I

tidied up the more mess I seemed to make. And when I couldn't cope with household things – I just used to dance. I danced by myself in my black underwear and my black shiny raincoat and wearing my red velvet hat like Frank Sinatra would have worn it.

I felt free like that and loose. It was even better when I smeared the lipstick with my fingers.

The messages were in the window for the cameras. So many messages, but I can only remember the knife dripping with blood saying, 'Amnesty For Ever'.

The next day everything started making cracking noises in my head. I felt strange.

My husband's drugging me, I thought. He's put it in the food. He's drugging her too. She's got bags under her eyes. She's so tired all the time. She's on heroin. Christ – she's on heroin!

I rang the school. They put me through from person to person.

'It has to be now. You have to do something now!' I shouted down the phone.

'We'll deal with it in due course,' they said. 'But just at the moment she is taking a GCSE exam.'

'I don't care. She's ill. I'm going to come now and bring her home.'

I put the phone down and ran to the car.

There was traffic. I put my hand on the horn and kept it there. Like before. But this time the cars wouldn't move. It was driving me insane. They just wouldn't move. I edged forward very gently and touched the car in front.

People were to say I had a crash and who am I to argue?

Then from nowhere police were walking towards me. I couldn't have chosen a better spot for the fracas with the car. I was right outside the police station.

People were looking at me – some vacantly, some with their eyes dancing. I couldn't understand how there could be so many people so quickly. I was sure one of them would help me.

'My daughter's on drugs and I can't get there!' I screamed at one of the smiling men.

Two policemen grabbed me. I twisted my legs in the railings. They were trying to pull me free.

'You'll have to break them!' I said.

They took me in and I talked to one of them in his office. I told him about the incest. He asked me so many questions. I can't remember any of them – but he wrote everything down.

The strangest thing of all was that my husband had seen the whole thing. I didn't know that then. They talked to him, but they believed me – and I was in the wrong.

Then I had to wait in a cell.

Whoever designed this cell had no imagination whatsoever, I thought.

It was a very obvious cell, concrete, graffiti, hard plastic bed and fag ends.

I thought I wouldn't waste time. I thought I'd do my exercises now – have a bath at home – and then go to the theatre. So I took my trousers off and started doing my yoga. After a while an officer came in.

'Put your clothes back on at once,' he said in a very shocked voice.

I was trembling a bit and so tired by now but they were

letting me go. They believed me. They would fix it. Then one of the policemen drove me home in my car.

Later my husband was to tell me how angry he'd been. He'd begged them to get a doctor for me – but they, the police, had told him to leave the area.

I was home and the phone was ringing. It was a newspaper wanting to ask me about the car crash.

'I've just left the police station,' I said. 'It only happened an hour ago. How did you hear about it?'

I told them there'd been no crash. I'd been stuck in a traffic jam. How can you have a car crash in a traffic jam? But he didn't believe me. The man on the end of the phone had a smile in his voice. Not a nasty smile, but he knew I was lying. There had been something, but I wanted to tell him it wasn't important.

I was beginning to feel very strange and my skin felt so dirty and I was burning up again. I felt on fire. My eyes felt scratchy all the time now and I couldn't stop. I couldn't stop destroying things.

I found a first-night present my husband had been given – an old '45 – there was an enigmatic message on it. It took me a long time – the hard plastic is practically indestructible. I used a hammer in the end.

Then I tore up all the pictures from one summer holiday because I thought – God knows what I thought. I made little bonfires and set them alight. My husband said when he came back that the kitchen and the patio were like a bomb site.

On that day – the last day – my daughter kept slipping in and out of the house, taking her bike with her. She'd leave for a while then return.

The phone would ring – she had an extension in her room by now. Later I was to discover that it was my husband warning her to leave the house because I was very sick.

Then the doctor phoned for me. I couldn't understand what she was talking about. I wasn't ill – what did she mean?

Then my daughter returned from her bike ride. My husband told me afterwards how furious he was that she'd returned to the house. He'd found her behaviour incomprehensible.

She must have loved me enough to know I'd never do her any harm. She was with me.

She went upstairs. The phone rang. Something strange had happened to the downstairs phone that day because when I lifted the receiver to listen – there was no click. She talked to her best friend quite naturally – not knowing I was listening.

'She's mad,' said my daughter. 'She's a bit different – but she's still mad.'

I put the phone down. It rang again.

A man's voice.

'Are you all right?' said the voice.

I didn't recognize it.

'Yes,' said my daughter.

'The doctors are coming,' he said. 'Get on your bike and cycle to the common – we'll meet you there.'

Christ! Oh, Christ! I thought. This is the end. The doctors are coming. The drug doctors. They're coming to inject her.

I called up. 'You're coming to the theatre with me.'

'I don't want to come!' she said.

I raced up the stairs, burst into her room and grabbed hold of her. We stumbled down the stairs together. She was resisting me but I pulled her towards the door.

'Can I put my shoes on?' she asked in a stricken voice.

'No, you can't!'

'Please, please can I put my shoes on?'

'No!'

She broke free. She was running away from me down the street. I chased after her. She was crying. I was screaming.

'You're on drugs!'

We ran – tears – breathless – down the street and round the corner.

She must have let me catch her because she can run like the wind. We stood there in the street. I was clutching her school skirt – the fabric all scrunched in my hand. She was hot and weeping.

A woman came down her front-garden path to speak to me.

'Oh, I do understand. My son was on drugs,' she said. 'Take her to the Sanctuary.'

I held her hard and so did the woman. We walked her back to the car. I held on to her. She was crying. She had no shoes.

One of my neighbours – having watched all the pulling and shouting and crying – said gently:

'Would you like to come into my house and sit down for a minute?'

I pushed my daughter down in the car seat.

'No,' I told her. 'I have to go to the hospital. I can't deal with anything any more.'

We drove to the Sanctuary. I dragged her roughly from the car when we got there.

I'd read somewhere that you have to be really firm and authoritative with drugs – and I wanted her to be too frightened of me to think of running away.

We went in. There was a handsome young American man on the phone at the desk. I thought it was a sign.

'My daughter's on drugs!'

I don't think I did any screaming. I can't remember very clearly – but what I can remember is a sense of enormous relief. I was in the right place. It felt even safer than the police station. I sat on the sofa near the desk – quite calmly. I wouldn't look at my daughter. I remember thinking I'd have to go straight to work and have a shower there – I'd have to go soon too.

'Could I make a phone call?' asked my daughter.

Her dad wasn't there. She talked to his best friend.

'I haven't got any shoes,' she said.

Then he arrived. My husband was there with another friend. Suddenly he was there. My daughter flew into his arms.

How I hated him – white-hot heat of hatred. He was screwing her and feeding her with drugs. I hated him and I screamed at them both:

'Poofs!' I screamed. 'They're going to lock you up and throw away the key!'

There in reception – in front of people.

Then I did as I was asked and went to sit in one of the drawing rooms. I was so happy then. I knew I'd be fine when I got to the theatre, especially when the curtain-up music started and I had my make-up on. I wouldn't be tired on stage and this was such a nice place. They'd cure her. There was everything you could possibly need – flowers – a ravishing fireplace – proper coffee and proper water – you could even have a cigarette – there were ashtrays everywhere.

What a nice, calm place, I thought.

After a while someone came to see me. I'd been wondering where everyone was.

At last, I thought. They've taken over and I can go to the theatre.

Then they started talking to me gently and led me imperceptibly down a long twisty corridor.

'I can't come,' I said. 'I can't come. I've got to go to the theatre – I've got a show to do.'

'No,' they said. 'You must come with us.'

There were so many of them. I think there were four. I'm only small, I thought. Why are they pulling me?

'It's all right, all right,' they said. 'We just want to talk to you – we won't be long.'

'Oh all right, but please phone the theatre and tell them I might be a bit late in tonight.'

I told them the name of the theatre and that I didn't know the number and that it was really important. They must have telephoned.

My understudy always got to the theatre in very good time. She did a lot of reading – she was nice – I liked her. But this time she didn't get there till the half. Poor cow. She must have died.

I was put in a room with a bed and a basin and a television. I went to the window – it didn't open. The room was just outside the desk with the nurses and the telephones.

So many people kept coming in to see me.

A social worker came in – his eyes were bored. And then another doctor came in. They kept asking me the same dreary questions. I told them over and over again about the light on the landing and the incest – but they kept asking me and asking me. Then yet another doctor.

'Do you mind,' I said. 'I am actually trying to watch *Channel Four News.*'

'Oh, sorry,' he said.

Then the family doctor came in. She must have come specially. She looked tired.

'You're on drugs, aren't you?' I said.

'No,' she said. 'I'm just tired.'

I kept explaining and explaining about everything. I didn't know why I had to say the same thing so many times.

They don't believe me, I thought. Why don't they believe me?

Then Doctor Darling came.

He was different from all the rest – his eyes burnt, blazed into mine. He didn't stay more than a minute. He went away and left me with some other doctor.

I wanted water but I couldn't drink from the jug because it was poisoned. So I ran the tap for ages and ages and ages because even the water in the tap was poisoned. I knew this – I knew about poison because every Christmas I was poisoned. I'd get the flu. My husband poisoned me every Christmas so he could go and see his other family.

I didn't like being shut in. I couldn't keep still. I couldn't stop moving. My heart was beating – boom boom boom. I had strange sensations in my throat.

People kept coming and going.

'Let me out! Let me out!' I screamed. 'I want to go – I want to go – it's a mistake!'

I started screaming.

'This is a prison!' I shrieked at them.

'No, it's not,' they said.

'Yes it is! A prison is where you can't get out.'

'There are no bars on the windows,' they said pleasantly enough.

'But I can't get out! I can't get OUT!'

More screaming. I remember Jeanne had to hold me still as I thrashed around.

'Let go of me! Just you let go of me! Stop it! I don't want to sit down. There's no law that says you have to sit down. Let go. Let me go! Now! Oh, all right, all right, all right, I'm only acting! Aren't I a good actress? You bought all that, didn't you? I'm now completely calm.'

She looked really miffed in a French sort of way and conceded that she'd believed me. For a fractured moment we were suspended – she'd been conned and I wasn't sick.

Doctors – more of them came. There was a look in their eyes – they were wary.

They needn't look like that, I thought. I won't hurt them. I wouldn't hurt anyone.

But I couldn't take any more. I still couldn't believe they weren't going to let me out. I knew I couldn't do it by myself but I had to try.

I pulled the mattress off the bed, lifted the iron bedstead up and tried to smash the window.

Doctor Darling was to ask me if I remembered. There

was admiration in his eyes as he enquired. I did remember – I remember most things but not all.

I knew then that they didn't believe me and that it was hopeless, but I had to keep fighting them. I felt I'd die if I just let them do as they wanted. I just couldn't give up.

But there were so many of them holding on to me. All in a circle. There were so many eyes. Their eyes were wet and shining.

Then I knew what would happen and it happened.

I saw the needle coming towards me.

It went into my arm and I didn't scream any more.

14

I woke up.

I was wearing a strange nightie, and someone had given me some clean knickers. They were men's boxer shorts made of some strange stiff gabardine material.

My clothes had gone and so had my money.

'You've taken everything!' I screamed at them. 'You've taken my clothes and my money and my pain. It was mine, the pain. I don't mind it. I can read when I'm depressed. I can concentrate.'

They stood there, two of them, in the doorway, looking back at me, and just for a split second they looked guilty. Unsure. But only for a second.

They wanted me to take pills and medicine but I wouldn't. So I had to have another injection.

It made me feel floaty and weirdly calm.

The woman in the next room was in the corridor. She slid up and down the wall.

'It's good exercise,' she said.

When she went on and on talking, I could feel my brain sliding away, but she seemed pleasant enough and I thought I'd better pretend to be kind.

She went into her room then and came out holding a red pepper, which she gave me.

The nurse looked so worried when I ate it.

I had a bath then without a flannel. I've never had a bath without a flannel before.

They didn't want to let me use the phone. I don't think they wanted me to upset people. Maybe, because I'd had a normal bath, they changed their minds.

I phoned home.

'Get me out of here, please,' I begged. 'I'm frightened. I don't like the drugs. They gave me an injection and orange medicine in a little cup. I'm frightened. Why can't I come home? I'll take my medicine at home. I promise I'll be good – just get me out of here.'

'I'll love you for ever,' said my husband. 'We'll look after you, but first you must rest.'

My daughter was on the line too.

'I love you Mama,' she said.

Everything was coming from so far away. I felt so doped up.

'I don't understand why we don't have coffee together any more,' I said.

'It was because you were working. We can have coffee. You've got to get better first and then we can have coffee again.'

'Promise?'

'Yes, but first you must sleep. They told me you must sleep to stop your mind racing. They said that was the most important thing.'

'Mama, we all have to do things we don't want to do. I've got to do my exams.'

'I've got to go now,' I said. 'There's a man, and he says I've got to stop talking. Phone tomorrow.'

The next day I did the Jack Nicholson trick of pretending to swallow my pills by hiding them under my tongue. I thought they'd see through that, but they didn't – or perhaps they did. There were lots of nurses, but I got to know Matthew, Mark, Luke and Jeanne best.

'You be good to us,' Matthew said, 'and we'll be good to you.'

They stopped the injections and I felt more like my old self. I felt strong and powerful again. I talked to myself.

Why are they doing this to me? Why am I locked up? Bastards! I only wanted them to test her for drugs. I've done nothing wrong. The business with the car was nothing. I'm not a danger to anyone. Why has he locked me up? I hate him. Where's my dad's gold watch? He's fucking sold it! I know all about him. I know all about his other life.

I'd get on and off the bed. I couldn't read. I couldn't watch the television. I couldn't even be bothered to smoke. I couldn't keep still. How could I manage days shut up like this, when I couldn't even manage minutes? Always the fluttery feeling in my chest – and the birds in my throat. Not knowing where to go. Not knowing what to do. Not knowing how to bear it.

And they wouldn't let me get dressed. They wouldn't give me back my jeans and brown boots. That made me angry.

I asked them for a knife to kill myself.

They probably thought I was acting – but I don't know whether I was or not. I felt like a wild animal all caged up. They gave me another injection.

When I woke there was a feeling in the pit of my

stomach that I didn't want to think about, but I couldn't push it down.

I was frightened of getting better.

I couldn't face the thought that I'd thrown away my life and my work and I wanted to stay with the Stranger. I wrote to him.

'Don't you want any money for the stamp?' I asked the nurses.

They gave me such a funny look.

I had to go to the loo then because Matthew had asked me very nicely to drink the juice to flush through the strong injection.

There was an old lady in the mirror. Her skin was grey. The right side of her mouth drooped slightly. She was finding it difficult not to dribble. There was no expression in her half-closed eyes. The old lady was me.

I was frightened. I wandered into the corridor.

'I want to go to a National Health hospital!' I begged them. 'I want to go now!'

They reeled back. I was never so mad that I couldn't see and understand the expression in people's eyes. They looked so shocked. It was as if I'd said I preferred Bedlam.

Medicine or no medicine, I thought, I am fed up with being pushed around by people with needles.

I lurched back to my room. Then something occurred to me. Perhaps they didn't like sticking in the needles? They never looked as if they were enjoying it. Maybe they minded that my arms were black and blue. Perhaps they wanted me to get better by myself – to accept the pills. And even though I knew drugs were dangerous, everyone else seemed all right.

I am not going to go under, I thought.

My family arrived. I didn't feel anything at all, only ice. I was sitting on the floor.

'You put me in here, didn't you?'

'I signed nothing,' he said.

'You know I don't want us to go on, don't you?' I said.

Nobody said anything for a long time.

'There is nothing much to say, is there?' I said. 'Will you excuse me now – I've got things to do.'

'Bye, Mum,' said my daughter. Her eyes were like glaciers.

That night I thought the Stranger was a dream and I thought he was going away for good. But he was so close when I woke up although I felt so implacably alone. I thought he was watching me all the time and that I was on the Internet. The radio was talking to me.

At three in the morning I thought I was a witch. I brewed tea and hung out with two other witches. Lalla and Maria.

'Double, double,' I said.

'What's for lunch tomorrow?' asked Maria.

'Shepherd's pie,' said Lalla. 'Unless they've run out of shepherds.'

We cackled away. We were a sight to see.

'You know what?' said Lalla. 'Peace is so much more than the absence of war.'

Witches we were as we sipped our brew.

Another night cocoa was late. Cocoa's at ten, but the nurse didn't make it then. The nurse made it late. I'd swallowed my dope, longing to chase it with a ciggie and cocoa. But by the time bedtime milk had arrived I felt very weavy, as if I were floating.

I used to think I was Joan of Arc of the Light for the

year 2000. I thought the television in the inmates' lounge could see me. I thought I'd put out my own bonfire cigarette with my fingertips, and I did so three times. I had the circular white weals to prove it.

'I want to try pain, but I'm not into masochism,' I told the Stranger as I stubbed out the cigarettes.

Then having smeared my lipstick to honour the poppy soldiers I set fire to a piece of clear blue paper and set off the hospital fire alarm.

The nurse was very cross with me.

I remembered a scene in *The Nun's Story* where Audrey Hepburn had a fight with a caged woman who thought she was the Angel Gabriel.

When they brought me two white pills and flicked on the flickering light to give me the medication, I thought the Stranger had turned my diamond ring into the palm of my hand along with the pills. They sparkled there like Holy Communion.

That was the fifth day. That night I crashed.

I belonged to them now and I did as they wished. They gave me dope and I gave in to it.

Then, at half-past seven, I fell through clouds of drowsiness. It was so delicious falling through layers and layers of sleep. It was a feeling I'd almost forgotten – from another time – a letting-go – a surrender. A different feeling – separate from being awake and busy – an escape. All of me limp – all mixed up in sheets and blankets.

Matthew and John came in with some more medicine later, and I struggled to the surface.

'We'll let her sleep,' I heard one of them say. 'We won't wake her up.'

15

My husband arrived. We went into a walled garden and sat in the June sunshine. He held my hand.

'You have manic depression,' he said.

We sat under a tree. I felt as if I were in a church beneath the sky. We spoke so quietly. It was so still.

'You've had it all your life,' he said. 'I wish I'd listened to you years ago when you told me there was something wrong with you.'

I thought it was normal to be very very happy or very very sad, and never in the middle. 'What did he say about me?'

'That you have flights of fancy, wild ideas and are writing reams of manuscript.'

'You mean, the letters?'

'Yes. But you're not usually violent.'

'Oh well, that's something.'

'All this is followed by a deep depression, sense of worthlessness, utter hopelessness.'

'You mean, either I'm nuts or I'm miserable?'

'That's about it.'

'Bloody hell!'

I didn't feel angry any more. I just felt splintered and so very glad to see him.

When you lose your way, when the things that hold you up fall down, there is no vanity any more – no ego. All the layers are stripped away. It's a dark place to live, but it's clean and clear.

You can spot the nurses who really care; a light of recognition shines out of their eyes, and with that light they give you back your dignity. The ones with the empty eyes, you see them too, but they haven't crossed over to where you are.

In the dark place you can feel the world of the others on the ward and there are no games. It's like a contract. Everyone is going in the same direction. It's like a never-ending dark moment in a play when time stands still, when there is so much power in the space, because the feeling between the audience and the actors is as one – all boundaries smashed. But in a play it only lasts for seconds. In a ward it lasts for days and nights.

When he left me sitting in the garden I thought for a while. I thought about my brain and how the illness affected it. Just then a blackbird touched down. He made me think about the crazy blackbird.

A long time ago we had a desperate crazy blackbird in our back garden. There was a mirror behind a tree and he'd fly straight at his reflection and crash, over and over again. It was distressing. We threw glasses of water over him, but back he came. Crash. I now knew why that had happened. The Stranger was the blackbird and when I took my baby home all those years ago he'd been angry. That's why he'd crashed into the mirror, to show me just how jealous he was.

I wondered if I'd ever change, even with the medicine. It was a frightening thought that I couldn't control my imagination. My imagination was me.

When you are high – when you are manic – everything has a meaning, a message. The sun going behind a cloud signals disapproval. Feeding the birds – the order in which they touch down has significance, and so does the power some birds have over others. You see the greed and monotony of the pigeons, as if they've been brainwashed. It's tiring and dispiriting to watch. Then down comes a jackdaw to declare war, a warrior jackdaw. Then a magpie, then a blackbird, and the pigeons scatter. It's as if some birds fly alone and you think they'll save the day.

But then your imagination changes course; from beauty you begin to deal in terror. It all becomes so sinister. The Coca-Cola machine in the dining room, so red and glowing, buzzes in the dark, eating money and pouring out liquid black cocaine – that's what I thought.

Then there were the arrows, little arrows on the sitting-room floor. There were little bits of paper pointing towards the dangerous people. It was nothing, of course, they were only bits of paper – sweet wrappings that people had dropped, but I thought they were warning arrows.

Only three people didn't have the arrows pointing towards them. The girl with the white scar slashes all over both arms.

'My mother abused me,' she said.

She smoked roll-ups and had the quietest eyes I have ever seen. She was a painter and I bought two of her paintings for fifteen quid. One picture of a black circle and one of a black square. I was going to frame them because they would look so right in the white sitting room I was going to live in with the Stranger.

The businessman wasn't dangerous either. He was the only one who liked *Newsnight* and we used to watch together in the sitting room.

There was one other – Joss – who was mad in a completely sane way. She was a life force. She was loud and she was lesbian. She was forever cheerful. Always cracking jokes. Perhaps she was happy because she fancied one of the nurses. She'd been a nurse herself. She liked playing her radio as much as I did. Sometimes the music was the only thing that kept you going.

In between our two rooms was Ariadne, who was the exact opposite of Joss. She never made any effort at all. She never washed. She didn't smell very nice. She never left her bed, except at mealtimes, when she pushed ahead, elbowing everyone out of the way. She was always complaining that she wanted more of her drugs. But when anyone tried to chat with her, all she'd say was:

'Help me, help me!'

Joss knew Ariadne loved chocolate and we thought that might help. She'd even sit up in her bed to eat chocolate. I got hold of some, but it was too chewy, her teeth kept sliding about.

'Help me, help me!' she said.

There wasn't much I could do. I wasn't putting my hand in there. Joss turned her radio on.

'Turn it off, turn it off!'

She demanded absolute silence all day long.

'We have rights,' said Joss. 'It's ten o'clock in the

morning. What's the matter with you? Why don't you go and have a bath?'

'Help me, help me!'

So that's what we called her – 'Helpme Helpme'. The nurses never chastised us. At least Helpme Helpme was awake because of us and might even have a bath.

Then it happened again. The radios were playing so quietly in our rooms and we heard:

'Nurse, nurse, they've started again! Help me, help me!'

Joss flipped. She strode in and said:

'Put a fucking sock in it!'

'Help me, help me!'

'The radio is staying on!' shouted Joss. 'If you don't stop moaning, I'll thump you!'

'Help me, help me!'

'Right, that's it,' said Joss, and thumped her.

I thought she'd gone too far. But Helpme Helpme didn't say, 'Help me, help me'; she said:

'Hit me, hit me!'

'Oh, you like that, do you?' said Joss. 'Right then.'

Wallop.

'Oh, lovely, lovely,' she groaned. 'Do it to me, do it to me.'

I nearly fell off my perch.

There are some weird people about and we all sat in the sitting room from time to time. It was really quite social. Some of us were more broken than others and nobody could sit still for long. There was an endless succession of Scrabble games started then abandoned and newspapers lying open and half-read and a pack of cards on the table.

I made another friend – Lee. She had big brown glittery eyes very heavily made up.

'I have a lover,' she said. 'He's very young, very black and absolutely gorgeous.'

She sparkled when she mentioned him.

I just wrote letters.

I wondered if she really did have a lover? When her husband came to see her, I watched them closely. I was none the wiser though because he was giving nothing away. It was as if he'd had the conversation a thousand times. She'd been in the Sanctuary before, this was her third time. Maybe she couldn't give up getting high even with medicine.

Then there was the doctor. He had restless eyes and paced a lot. He kept coming into my room and I felt mean asking them to stop him. He didn't intend any harm, he only wanted to talk, but it happened over and over.

He left my room and rattled the fire-escape door.

'Why is this locked?' he asked. 'It shouldn't be locked.'

This was exactly what I'd done in the hotel. I recognized the demons in his feet. He was a surgeon. I wouldn't want anyone with this illness cutting me up.

I moved then. That was how it worked, one progressed from room to room. Once I'd given in they were quite pleased with me. I bathed every morning and made my bed and tidied my room.

They'd taken my dressing-gown belt away from me, and having it flap open all the time was driving me mad. I found a length of plastic wire in the wardrobe and tied it up with that. Jeanne noticed this and got my belt back for me. She was remarkably forgiving. I'd been so rude, so unpleasant. Yet she was so ordinary with me when I got better. She bore me no grudge. She didn't dismiss or negate my behaviour, but she seemed to imply that it was separate from me.

'Ça va?' she'd ask, whenever I went down the carpeted corridor and passed her office.

'Oui, ça va, ça va.'

The Sanctuary was a cross between a hotel and a chapel. You got no feeling of Big Brother. You could make yourself a cup of tea whenever you wanted to, or use the hot-water machine to fill a hot-water bottle. It was early summer but I could never get warm. Outside they were playing croquet on the lawn.

They let me use the phone after a few days. They gave me my coins for the phone – or did they? Perhaps they let me use their phone. I can't remember. I phoned the man with the deep voice. I was so worried about the play and letting everyone down. This time it wasn't an answerphone. I heard his voice, crisp and terse. I didn't know what to say.

'It's the play,' I said. 'You see, it's the play. I can't bear just leaving it unfinished. It's so unprofessional.'

I told him where I was ringing from, and however hard I tried I couldn't stop crying.

'Oh, darling,' he said. 'Poor darling.' He wasn't terse any more. 'Not to worry, not to worry, just you get better,' he said. 'Anyway, sod it, the understudy will go on. That's what they're for. You poor darling.'

'They had to take me away.'

'I know,' he said in a very deep voice. 'I know.'

So kind, so good. He was with me down the wire. Just

for a few seconds it wasn't so bad. There was him. At least there was someone, because I couldn't find the Stranger any more. The injections had taken him away and they'd also taken away the cameras. He couldn't see me any more. I tried writing to him, but I tore the paper to bits.

I felt myself melting into reality. It was frightening.

What I can't remember is when or how it transpired that I was asked to leave the play. I can't even be sure that when I telephoned the big boss the conversation really happened or whether I dreamt it. I can remember being put straight through and that he was kind and normal.

'I do understand,' he said. 'Don't worry, it's all right, it's all right.'

'Will I be paid?' I asked. 'It's so expensive in here.'

'Of course you will.'

I didn't want to leave the production, but they had to recast, and even I could see that it would be too much like gambling. I might make a dreadful mistake.

Then the theatre doctor came to see me. I gave a rational performance and carried on a normal conversation. He said he'd given up smoking for Lent. We talked about that for a bit. But I didn't like him seeing me in my dressing-gown.

I realized then that the stakes were too high. I'd have to get used to the real world first before I could go back to the dream one.

'It will take time,' said Doctor Darling. 'You've never been as high as this for so long before. The brain decides independently how long it needs for restoration after so long a spell up.'

Sitting and thinking about my broken brain was

counter-productive, so I wandered about a lot in the grounds. They have a lot of trouble with pigeons at the Sanctuary, so there are two metal statues of hawks on the roof. These turn by clockwork, and they seem reasonably effective, but the pigeons are pretty persistent and sometimes sterner measures are needed.

One morning I was strolling about when I met the falconer. At his command the falcon would dive-bomb all over the place, frightening the shit out of the pigeons.

I knew I was an eagle.

The Stranger was an eagle too. Not at that moment, not at the Sanctuary, before. The man with the deep voice had told me over the radio. I had heard him loud and clear.

'But you are eagles,' he'd said.

I wasn't frightened remembering the radio voices in the sunshine. I wasn't ashamed either.

We talked, the falconer and I, for quite a long time. The falcon seemed to be listening to the conversation. Then he fed the bird chicks that had never been born, stroking his head with his finger. Then he put a little hood over the falcon's head and lowered him into a basket which he placed on the back seat. It seemed a bit hard to make the bird go to sleep in broad daylight if he didn't want to. But what did I know? Bird and man obviously adored each other.

It wasn't a spooky place, the Sanctuary, people were just people. They weren't particularly mad, they were just broken. I felt fearfully sorry for the Middle Eastern gentleman who moaned all the time, but I got over it. He was enormous, mountains of flesh. He'd had a hip operation which had gone wrong. The moment several staff had got him comfortable, arranging his arms and legs, he'd want to sit somewhere else and they'd have to start all over again.

The man with the kindness in him – I liked him a lot. He'd been in before, many, many times, and he seemed more part of the staff than the patients. He'd keep getting sick time and again, because he'd inhaled too many fumes for too many years from a certain glue used to stick down lino. It had affected his brain. I wanted to do some weeding and he got me a hoe. He was in charge of equipment – equipment was considered dangerous.

The next day we went for a walk. At one point we were so near my house.

'I live over there,' I told him.

'That's nice,' he said.

'If I pick up speed,' I said, 'if I run and then hide – I could go home.'

'Don't be stupid,' he said. 'You've been sectioned for twenty-eight days.'

Then I was moved into my third and last room. I was allowed to get dressed.

I hate going to 'improve thyself' gatherings, but I thought I'd better go to a few. If I really behave, I thought, they might let me out. I started having long, boring conversations with rather old ladies suffering from depression – so they could see how charitable I was. In fact, whenever there were doctors or nurses about, I made a point of being absolutely adorable to everybody. I went to a flower-arranging class run by the cheeriest of cheerful souls it has ever been my misfortune to meet. She was so enchanting, I wanted to smash her face in. When your life's in bits on the floor the last thing you need is to be grinned at all the time.

My God, I thought, I'm normal again.

But then I thought I'd better calm down or they'd make me get back into my dressing-gown and change rooms.

There were flowers everywhere and smelly old flower water and crazy people being floppy and fiddling about.

I will not be beaten, I thought. Even though I do not know anything about arranging fucking flowers – I'll bloody well do it.

The cheery lady was smiling away and chattering. I kept sticking all these flowers into the wire. It didn't look very good. In fact it looked terrible. But the whole thing was getting gratifyingly bigger. There were yawning gaps, though; my creation seemed to have too many holes. We'd all been allocated a certain amount of flowers, and I don't know what came over me, but I nicked my neighbour's Sweet Williams. She was having a vague sort of day and I knew she wouldn't notice. So as a result my flower erection looked absolutely brilliant and it was placed in reception. Every time I walked past it, I got a huge thrill.

There wasn't much else to do except wander about. I had clothes and they trusted me not to run away. There had been a chapel there once, but it was now changed into a boardroom. That was a great disappointment, although there was a trace of the atmosphere left. I went to a relaxation class. It didn't work for me. The voice went on and on and I felt tenser than before. Pity about the chapel.

I asked Lee to read the cards for me one afternoon. She got the deck out and the nine of hearts fluttered to the floor. It was a strange and welcome card to fall. It didn't matter what the rest of them said, although she said it was a good reading. I wanted to know if I'd ever meet the Stranger. I wanted to tell him how very sorry I was and to apologize, not least to his wife.

16

They let me out.

I think it was VAT that convinced Doctor Darling that I was ready to leave.

My husband had brought my papers the day before, all the tedious bits of paper you need for doing VAT. It was six days late, the sodding VAT. They'd sent me a letter saying they were going to let me off the prosecuting hook, or whatever it is, if I paid up pronto.

Oh, thank you *very* much! I thought. How very kind. I happen to have had a VERY hairy nervous breakdown, and I'm frightfully sorry to have kept you waiting. *Do*, DO forgive me. I wouldn't dream of upsetting you and your dreary money for the world.

When they came to call, all the doctors, there was paper as far as the eye could see. It was everywhere.

Oh God, I thought, all this mess. They'll think I've gone nuts again.

But one of them said:

'Ah, finances.'

'You can go this afternoon,' said the doc.

'What!'

'You can go home,' he said. 'I thought I'd save you some money.'

I'd been sectioned for twenty-eight days, but they were letting me out in thirteen.

There was an explosion of joy in my chest. It was so unexpected. I was in a state of happy shock.

'You must give yourself a break,' said the doc. 'You're a perfectionist. You must be easy on yourself and those around you.'

'I can't help it,' I said. 'It has to be the best I can do. I can't phone things in.'

'The pills will help.'

He handed me a photostatted three paragraphs about the Greeks, about moderation and not competing. I'd sent a photostatted three paragraphs about Zen to the Stranger. Same thing really.

He really is a very special man. He's top-dog doctor at the Sanctuary and he flies all over the place, all over the world, talking about why people go nuts.

How do they know so much?

I packed up. I left all the cards people had sent. I left my soap. I never wanted to go back. The taxi came and we went home.

I was still a little high when I got home. The first thing I did was to repot a plant. I'd found one just the right size in a skip near the Sanctuary and I changed the soil. But then I stepped backwards and knocked over a big brass bowl of pot pourri – dead petals everywhere.

Something snapped. The birds in the throat came back. I couldn't keep still.

'I want to play Scrabble,' I said. 'I want to play Scrabble now!'

'Half of it's missing,' said my husband. 'We'll go and get a new one.'

So we did. But it was no use. I couldn't sit still long enough even to sort the letters out. I swallowed another pill. I stood in front of the bookcase picking out book after book.

'I can't concentrate,' I said. 'What's happening? I can't read more than a page.'

'It's all right, we'll watch a film,' he said.

One scene swam into another and the whole thing was completely meaningless.

It was still there the next day, the restlessness, the need to keep moving. So we drove to the theatre to collect my things. It was like trying to keep afloat in a boiling sea.

I had to retrieve my things, my make-up and my bits, my presents and my cards. My soap wasn't in the dish. You never leave your soap in a theatre even if it's only a sliver. If you do it means you'll never go back.

The heat of the summer sun made my skin feel too tight as I got out of my car and walked towards the stage door.

Oh Christ, I thought. I've got to go in there.

I hated people knowing that I was too ill to stay in the play. I'd found that people do one of two things. They look at you in one of two ways. Some look ashamed and furtive because . . . I suppose everyone talks, and everyone is afraid of madness . . . but some are less afraid and look into your eyes.

I walked in.

Eric, the company manager, was unafraid, and his eyes looked straight into mine, but the others looked away and I felt dirty.

Why I felt my heart had split in two when I got home, I don't know. After all, it was only make-up and little bottles and the glittery butterfly that I always twisted round an old green bottle my husband had bought me in '75. Everything was all muddled up. They were only things but they were all mixed up. My make-up case was just a jumble, everything tangled up. I'd always packed it and packed it in a special way. My part was in there, and someone else had my part. She was a friend too. The last time I'd seen her she'd been so out of work. I introduced her to someone important standing next to me at a party and now she had my part. But I hadn't finished playing it, and whoever it was had muddled up my things, they'd touched my things. There were things in there from thirty years ago, things from my first job.

And it was so hot, so hot. I don't remember driving home.

'They're only things,' my husband said. 'You haven't lost what's important.'

I couldn't look in the bag at first. I couldn't sort it out. But I know that if I get another job, I'll be absolutely ruthless and quite sanguine about recreating the order of my things. This part will be quite without relevance. I can pretend to be someone else again.

For me acting is time off – an excuse for not having to think the same dreary thoughts over and over again. My thoughts – my observations. I know what I think, I've been there so many times. So to stand in as proxy for a master of make-believe, and make his world a reality, is time off from my own endless thoughts. But then I wonder if I can do it. They've paid, the audience, and they're stuck with me for two whole hours. Will they believe me? That's when I try to go up. I'm a little high when I'm trying to understand and learn a part. A cracking part has magic in it – and magic is hard to get hold of, to pin down. Wherever it is, it isn't in me – it's outside. So I put on the headphones, brew up some coffee, light up a cigarette and stare at the words.

I'm in two places at once, my brain is racing and the lines aren't grounded. They're separate from me and it isn't a question of how I should say them, but how they should be said. Then it won't be me saying them but somebody else. I don't want to get in the way of the man who made the play. The one who made something out of nothing. I don't want to be a middlewoman, I want to be a channel, open to the outside and not in the way.

Those are the blissful times, legalized fantasy.

My head goes on holiday, I don't have to think my mouse-on-a-wheel thoughts – I can borrow someone else's. But you have to go up. You can't wash socks and then say: Oh for a muse of fire. Well I can't.

Are we mad?

I heard an actor on the radio once. The Dalai Lama had asked him:

'When you are angry in your work – are you really angry or are you acting?'

'Both,' said the actor. 'You are both. You can be opposite things at the same time.'

If I were to lean close into someone's face and scream: 'I am so angry with you!' he wouldn't like it, even if I'd told him what I was going to do before I did it. The person on the receiving end gets the reality mixed up with the pretence.

That's what I love most about being an actress. I like joining everything up. It's my job and it's very practical. I like saying to the darkness, the darkness filled with shadowy people:

It's all right. Whatever you feel, it's been felt before. It will be felt again. It will be all right. If you are afraid that there is something wrong with you, let me pretend to feel it for you. If I do it well, you'll forget things for a while. You can have a rest, and we'll all be joined up. Just like when the Soldiers of Song go marching.

'Captain says there'll be a bust.'

Piano – trumpets.

Wanderlust.

'The splashdown is coming, I'm afraid,' said Doctor Darling a few days later.

We were sitting in comfortable armchairs, the sun streaming in through his office windows.

'The depressive phase will take you down very far.'

'It's all right, I'm used to it,' I said.

'But you've never been up so high for quite so long, so prepare yourself.'

'I'll be all right when the winter comes.'

'Why is that?'

'I like it when it gets dark and we draw the curtains and turn on the lights. I feel safe then.'

'You can't stop the illness once it has started, but the lithium, hopefully, will stop the next cycle beginning. However there's nothing I can do to stop this cycle.'

'I went out of my mind, didn't I?'

'Well, yes.'

We walked home across the park.

17

❦

The depressive part of manic depression is the exact opposite of the mania. From not being able to sleep, I could no longer stay awake. My bed was a burrow. Opening my eyes in the morning to face the day was like trying to walk through the water of an incoming tide. He was right, I was down very far.

Then I wasn't walking through a tide, I was under the water. Thoughts would swim to the surface through green slime. I felt I'd committed a crime. I felt it was my fault I had manic depression. But even as I thought that, I'd deny it to myself. It was a mistake. I'd wake up soon and be happy again like I used to be.

I didn't know who I was any more. Thinking was so tiring. I just wanted to doze on the sofa.

'Are you awake?' he'd ask.

'Yes,' I'd lie.

Going to bed with a book I'd read before, the words dancing, I'd try to stave off the morning with reading. But it was no good. Sleep would come too soon. So there was no gap between the blistering days.

Then the tears came, they came unbidden, with no

warning. I kept refusing to accept it had happened, trying to explain it, to justify it.

'It's no use,' he said. 'It happened.'

But then we remembered talking on the telephone at the Sanctuary.

'Please, please, I want to come home.'

'Darling, you can't, you can't come home yet.'

We wept together.

How strange that a person's will, or whatever it is that makes a person a person, should be entirely separate from his brain. The brain makes its own decisions. If it has been too tired, too burnt, for too long a time, it will decide itself how much rest it needs. Doctor Darling told me that.

I began to understand. If I was sad and tearful and lazy, it meant I couldn't speed, and if I couldn't speed it meant I would get better.

How can my will and my brain be separate? I don't know. I do know I didn't want to stay under the water.

But it was so hot making an effort. It was scorchingly, horribly, implacably hot. The garden was withering away and so was the park where we walked. God, how we walked. I was pretty drugged up and we had to keep stopping. The hinges in my knees weren't working very well, but we walked for miles.

'Keep her out of the kitchen,' Mark, one of the nurses, had said to my husband.

It didn't matter. I'd forgotten how to cook. Anyway I was never hungry.

'You must eat.'

'I can't taste anything.'

'You must try!'

Just agree with him, I thought, but then when I forgot, the anger would flare up and flash at him.

'I feel you're my keeper!'

Then it would be all right until the next time. He looked so worn, his face so dark. The house had the oddest atmosphere, a sort of ominous stillness, as if there had been a battle fought.

It was better getting out. I drove the car. It was quite scary driving, because I had to concentrate. However slow I went it felt too fast. The wheel felt so heavy, and the traffic was whirling all round me. We parked the car and went to buy a gold bracelet.

'I've been traumatized,' our daughter had said. 'I need a gold bracelet.'

As fate would have it we bumped into my daughter's teacher. She seemed kind, but she was so shy and looked only at the ground. She can't even meet my eyes, I thought. I wondered when it would end though, the horror, the numbness.

It wasn't ending yet. Doctor Darling had advised my daughter to go away for a fortnight so that she could recover from it all. She could only get better away from me. That was the final thing. The thought that she could only get better away from her mother. It was like being knifed but I couldn't feel the blade. I felt numb. It felt like I was falling from a long way up and there was nothing I could do. I'd always been her sanctuary and now she could only find it away from me. That was very hard to accept.

She was wary with me before she left for France to stay with friends. The look in her eyes was guarded. Then one night she asked me if I'd like us to watch a video together with her friend. I was to have the sofa. She tucked me up with a blanket and they cooked the popcorn. She kept offering me more and more.

'Are you all right, Mum?' she asked. 'Do you want some of my salsa dip? Are you enjoying the film?'

'Yes, it's a really good film, but I can't concentrate very well.'

'When you were in the hospital, Mum, I couldn't concentrate either. I couldn't even watch *Neighbours*.'

We talked later that evening. I was trying to explain something that had happened.

'You must think of your illness like a balloon,' she said. 'All the illness is in the balloon. If you take one thing out of the balloon and try to make sense, it won't work. Anyway, I like you better now. You were shouting then and going hurrah very loudly at the telly.'

And then she was gone.

It was sad at home. Her room stayed so tidy, so horribly tidy, and there'd be stilted phone calls to France. I'd hear her chatting away to her dad for hours and then she and I would have nothing to say.

I replaced the phone in her room and sat on her bed. Once the cat used to jump on the bed for the story. It was psychic that cat. Its timing was immaculate. I thought those days would last for ever. The routine, the sweet-scented child, the book, the cat and the bedside light. The exquisite order of things.

'Once upon a time, in the olden days, there was a very naughty princess . . .'

'No, no, Mama, you're wrong. These are the olden days. The ones before came first, so they were new.'

After a lengthy philosophical discussion I caved in.

'Once upon a time, long long ago when the days were new . . .'

At last, she and the cat started to nod off. I stayed for a while and then crept away.

'I'm still awake.'

'GO TO SLEEP!'

'If you love people you shouldn't shout at them.'

Now I left the empty room knowing I could never lean on such order again. She was grown now and didn't need me in the same way as before.

I had to make friends with chaos. I knew now why I hated the flowers in the garden. They spelt mayhem. They were frightening. Their colours shouted at me, and so did the sun burning them up. I looked at a rose and all I could think of was the sun roasting it to death.

The trees in the park were all right except for their leaves. The trunks so grey and rough to touch. I put my arms around one as my husband walked on and I could feel its strength seeping into me. I caught him up and we walked on, always the same way, to the sacred place. The pond.

There was a particular pond, partly hidden amongst the bracken. If you sat still the deer would go on drinking and sometimes the heron would be there. It was drying up, more and more each day, but there was something special about it. It was still, suspended. I'd lie in his lap. Thoughts would turn themselves around in our heads and we'd voice them.

'I feel so awful about the letters,' I said. 'It won't go away. I feel so ashamed I pestered someone. I feel so stupid.'

'It takes courage to make a complete idiot of yourself,' he said. 'And anyway, it's not as if you phoned him up or stalked him. They were only letters.'

'I feel such a fool.'

'I wouldn't worry about it any more,' said my husband. 'He probably didn't even read them.'

That really cheered me up. For one thing I'd spilt my soul on to those pages, and for another, I'd gone nuts.

'Oh, fuck it!'

'That's more like it,' he said.

'Right! I'd better get my will out from wherever it lives,' I announced. 'I'm going to do the hardest thing I can think of. I'm going to take over the chores, and I'm going to do it on my own.'

'Yes, go for it.'

I'd walk to do the shopping, taking a particular carrier bag. I got very attached to that carrier bag. I didn't take the car. The trouble was I kept bumping it. I'd lost the parking knack. It wasn't too bad, though, walking. I looked at all the stressed-out drivers boiling up in their cars waiting for a space. I could just breeze in, but then I had to concentrate on the shopping list. The items on it would dance about in front of my eyes, but I'd pin them down if it killed me.

I thought of the man with the list who couldn't read his wife's handwriting. She'd written 'parakeet livers'. He looked for ages and then he asked everyone, delicatessen, store manager – no luck. When he got home he told her he couldn't find any parakeet livers.

'What's the matter with you?' said his wife. 'That says "pedal-bin liners".'

Maybe I was in a film. Maybe I was Anne Bancroft in *The Pumpkin Eater* bursting into tears in Harrods Food Hall. That was a good scene – depressing, though. So I thought of a Marx Brothers film instead.

'The garbage men are coming in the morning.'
'Tell them we don't want any!'

I bought some grapes. For some reason I had to make a fruit salad every day. God knows why. I'd get all the other dreary, boring bits of food we needed and go to the checkout. Very calm, very ordered, very thorough.

I was putting the food on the moving shelf when the checkout lady said:

'Are you all right, love? I saw something in the paper. Are you all right now?'

I promptly burst into tears. When strangers were kind it was hard not to cry. But they were clean tears, not depressive ones, and doing the little bit of shopping made me feel better.

The bag was heavy in the heat as I walked home.

I met a lovely old actress, someone I'd worked with on the radio. Between scenes we'd had long chats about her lover from long ago.

'How are you?' she asked.

'I'm fine,' I said. 'How are you?'

'Fine.'

I told her a little of what had happened and how I'd blown it in the play.

'Oh, you're allowed one mistake,' she said.

'I've got to take pills to keep me on the planet.'

'I've got to take pills too,' she said. 'I've just been diagnosed with Parkinson's.'

Bloody hell, I thought. When sorrows come, they come not single spies, but in battalions!

I went home and peeled the grapes.

Later we went to see Doctor Darling. It was good to see him, but it was almost impossible not to relive being shut away. But being ex-boarding-school it seemed natural somehow to make the best of things.

It was difficult to know what to say to the doctor. To tell him honestly that I didn't have the puff to put all the broken bits of my life back together again, or to say I was trying as hard as I could. The latter seemed the better choice.

'I'm very pleased about the walking,' he said. 'A lot of patients just sit in a heap and stare into space.'

'Oh, I'm very good at that too,' I said. 'But I did do the shopping yesterday. I started the list, but then I got bored, and when I came back, it just said nuts and bananas.'

'I'm glad your sense of humour is coming back.' He laughed. 'But it's going to be hard. It's a case of three steps forward and two steps back.'

He knew me better than I knew myself. My husband would watch him watching me.

'My clothes feel funny,' I explained. 'I feel sort of graceless and dark – as if I'm in the way – and it's hard doing things round the house. I can't do them to music because the music hurts so much.'

But he knew all about the worthless feeling.

'I'll give you something with a little more zest in it,' he said.

So I swallowed all my pills each evening and trundled on.

It was strange hating all the things I'd loved before: being in the house, food and the garden. I didn't like the garden any more. I didn't like nature. In fact, I'd gone right off nature. It seemed so unruly, so arrogant and garish.

My life narrowed down to the sharpest of angles, and the only thing I loved now was water. I liked looking at the pond in the park. It didn't intrude, it just lay there making no demands. When we got home I liked the coolness of it as I washed away the dust that had got between my toes through my sandals as I walked. I couldn't get enough of it into me. It tasted like a drink for the gods. The pills made me thirsty so I drank all the time. I'd wake in the night and drink. The water would hit the back of my throat and I could feel it sliding down into my stomach. There was relief and release in putting out the fire of thirst. As I fell asleep again, everything narrowed down to the glass of water.

I can wake up soon and drink some more, I thought.

It was something to look forward to.

18

August came, it got hotter and we left for France.

The taxi driver took us a funny way to the station, but I didn't say anything. The train was sleek and so was the magazine I bought. I didn't read it though. I looked out of the window as England unfolded. Moving was wonderful. It was a holiday for my eyes and my thoughts. I didn't feel guilty, because I wasn't idle, I was busy watching. There was a flicker of feeling I might belong in the world again one day. I might be part of it all, not separate and cut off.

So we went to the sea, under the sea.

We picked up speed in France and unlike my head the train didn't rattle and roll when it went so fast. It was very calm on the train – time out of time. I looked for wild poppies from the window. I like poppies. I like being reminded of the dead soldiers. I don't find it depressing. By the time we arrived at Gare du Nord I felt quite smoothed out. It was the sky, the calm people and the cool train.

Then we stepped out of the taxi into a furnace. I longed for the winter in the unbearable heat at Gare

Montparnasse. The TGV was full of Polish Catholics on their way to Lourdes. This was real religion, not the smooth spirituality I'd been feeling. There was no order in the carriage. There was noise and an overpowering smell of food. Across the way a woman was cutting up a tomato. It squelched all over her blouse. She cleaned it off with bottled water and spilt that too. Then she gave a fistful of francs to the priest, who never said thank you. Afterwards they read their Bibles.

It was horrible. It was so messy. It was life. I envied them their ease in all the chaos. We got off at Dax and travelled on to where France turns the corner into Spain. They went left to Lourdes.

The next day we walked through the town to the bay.

'How was your year?' asked the Spanish count on the beach.

'Fine,' came the cagey reply. 'How was yours?'

'It was like being looked at by a one-eyed man.'

'Did you make that up?'

'No. Cervantes did.'

The same people, Australian, French and Spanish, float in and out of each other's lives every summer by the sea in France.

How I loved the sea, gazing at the water for hours. The great thing about the sea is its indifference. Why should that be so reassuring? Perhaps because it leaves me in peace and the sea doesn't make any demands. Not only that, I don't have to mow it or hoover it either.

The Atlantic waves are magnificent. I managed to catch one. My husband showed me how. He'd been taught by the Australian, Bondi. He said Bondi was the best bodysurfer he'd ever seen. I put my flippers on and swam out beyond the waves. Waiting in the sea for my wave I looked behind me.

'Swim!' shouted my husband. 'Go! Now!'

I swam like the clappers and caught it. It was like being plugged into an electric current. The water was on fire and hurled you forward. It was a bit frightening really, like being shot out of a gun. It was not unlike being high – out of control and possessed by something else.

It was fun.

On my way back to the steps, the steps everyone sat on, I saw a woman I knew.

'Hello,' I said.

'*Bonjour, madame.*'

'How has your year been?' I asked.

'*Bien, et vous?*'

'Oh, I had a nervous breakdown. I went completely *noisettes.*'

She fled for a swim. When she came back she was a bit cautious, but we chatted again.

'I am so sad,' she said. 'My computer has something wrong with it.'

'Why don't you kiss it?' I suggested. 'It worked with my video recorder.'

'*Vraiment?*' She laughed.

Everything was all right again. Funny that. Say something crass and everything is fine. Tell the truth and it's like throwing a hand grenade.

We sat on the steps as the tide came up the beach. The aficionados knew the score. The best bit was watching other people's belongings get all wet. When the tide was fully in, the waves crashed over the low wall. The red flag went up – no more swimming today. The smaller children crouched at the foot of the wall and screamed with terror and delight as they got drenched by big waves. My daughter used to do that.

When they were all little they used to walk up to the nude beach. 'We saw some people sexing,' they said. 'We saw their bottoms.'

It was good in France. There were so many people. It was good discipline. I didn't think I could do it but I did. I could act that I had something to say. I could act that I wasn't frightened of people. Everyone knew what had happened and they were greatly relieved that I didn't want to talk about it all the time.

'You should write it down,' said Bondi.

'I can't,' I said, 'it was chaos.'

'Well, it would prove you were better.'

I wasn't supposed to have a lot of *vin*, it didn't mix with the pills. The doctor had said I could have just one glass. So I did and it did something to my head. It made it go all black and angry. We had a terrible row in the *jardin public*.

'It's all right for you,' I shouted, jumping up and down between the flowerbeds and pointing at my head. 'I'm off me bonce!'

My husband collapsed with laughter and then I got the giggles.

It was cold-turkey time. *La belle France* without her wine was hard. It was an insult to me and an insult to France.

'Here's to what's coming,' said the count, holding his glass high one evening.

I had to raise a glass of water to this wonderful gypsy toast.

Fuck that, I thought. I'm having a slug of wine.

The Australians were there and so were the count's mum and dad – the duke and duchess. They are old, they speak flawless English and are very gracious. We sat round eating paella.

'Nice fish,' said Bondi.

'Do you remember when you ordered three trout in French and said "*twa tweet*"?' I asked.

'The waiter knew exactly what I meant.'

The duchess was intrigued that I had once worked with Vivien Leigh and wanted to know all about her.

'I can't tell you very much,' I said. 'I can tell you what I noticed though.'

'Please do.'

'She smoked Olivier cigarettes and she had his photograph on her dressing-room table.'

'Do you think she still loved him?'

'Yes, I think she did,' I said. 'She let me watch a friend of mine on her hotel television once. I was in digs. I went up to her room and she answered the door with no shoes on. It was very formal in those days. I was nineteen and she was my age now. You had to call her Miss Leigh. I mentioned I'd just seen one of her films at the Classic Cinema.'

'Which film?' asked the duchess.

'*Fire Over England*,' I said. 'I thought she'd be pleased, but I think it just made her feel old. I wish I'd kept my mouth shut now. I can't remember any more. What struck you most was her fragility. She was almost unknowable. I expect it was the pills.'

We rose to leave and crowded into the lift together with the count's two Jack Russells. We were all being very silly in three languages.

The lift stopped.

The lift was stuck.

We were stuck in the lift.

My throat closed. My heart was banging in my chest. My breathing came fast and shallow. It was almost unendurable. I was in a steel vice. It was worse than the needles and worse than being trapped in the Sanctuary.

The duchess held my hand.

'I don't like it,' I heard my voice saying.

'Would you like to go to your husband?' she asked.

'Yes, please.'

There were eight people and two dogs in a lift for five. Everything was incredibly clear. Façades fell away. Everyone became utterly real and you saw what people were truly like.

The dogs were puzzled, concentrating very hard on the doors, but they behaved beautifully. The duke and duchess were effortlessly stoical, quite impassive and very dignified.

'There's a hammer in the boot of the car,' said the duke to the count. 'Use the lift phone to get hold of the chauffeur.'

'What good's a hammer?' asked the count. The rest of the conversation took place in Spanish.

My husband seemed more preoccupied with our present predicament than with anything else.

'We're stuck between floors,' he said. 'There's a gap. Look, we can breathe.'

Bondi said he could break the frosted-glass panel with his hand-made shoe. His wife lowered her head silently. The count and his Spanish friend were masterful. He picked up the phone and rattled away to the *pompiers* in rapid French, reassured us in English, and had a word or two to his dad in Spanish.

'Please tell them,' I said, '*nous avons peur, nous avons beaucoup de peur.*'

I was screaming silently in my head and nearly cracked, but somehow kept control. I just didn't want the only person to crack to be English. I didn't want to be the one. If they could take it, so could I.

'Ssh,' someone said. 'I can hear something.'

There were muffled sounds in the distance. We started banging and shouting. I liked that bit. If I couldn't scream, at least I could shout. Then there was some shuddering and the lift jerked. The light in the hallway came on and a face shimmered through the glass panel.

'*Excusez moi,*' we shouted. 'Hello, hello, *bonjour, bonsoir!*'

Miraculously the doors opened and I pushed myself forward and flung my arms around a startled French lady in a dressing-gown.

'Oh, *merci, merci . . .*' I said. '*Nous étions absolument* completely terrified.'

I think she thought I'd gone *bananes* because I kept on hugging her. I even hugged one of the *pompiers* when we got outside. He looked so disappointed at having nothing to do.

The night air was cool and took the panic away. The sky was clear, there was no wind. It meant tomorrow, our last day, would be fine.

I knew how it would be. We'd swim our last swim and climb the cliff to the top and then turn round for one last look.

Each time you caught sight of the bay it cut you and your problem down to size. The tamarisk trees grew all the way down the cliff. The coastline curved as it swept into Spain. The sea sparkled and the mountains beyond shimmered in the haze. The waves crashed in slow motion and the black rock stuck out of the sea. The grandeur pushed all the little thoughts out of your mind. It never palled, it never disappointed, it always lifted you up.

19

It rains.

I hear the tyres swishing.

As I write this, my skin cools with the sweat that breaks when I read things I wrote when I was mad. Poor husband – poor Stranger. He'd sent two letters back in which I'd said that, whilst he was a diamond, my husband was an emerald – and that the assassins were coming. He probably wanted me to get help. The accompanying note was terse. My husband read not a word.

The clock ticks as I write about what happened to me. About the crack-up. I look out of the window and think about how busy everyone is, everyone I know. But perhaps some of them are looking out of windows too.

I really should get on and tidy up my house and my life.

I am not mad. I have never been mad, not even nor'-nor'-west. I have manic depression, I have a soluble problem. I must swallow the salt and remember not to overdose on beauty.

I have the lithium now and it isn't even a drug. It's a salt. Doctor Darling explained about lithium. I don't understand it exactly, but if water is fizzing and bubbling and you put lithium into it, it calms and stills it.

Doctor explained something else. Manic depression turns two and two into five and you believe absolutely that five is four.

'I'm glad I caught you in time,' he said. 'Otherwise I couldn't have brought you back. You were on the outer limits of exhaustion.'

But I never minded paying the price for going high, and it seems a shame somehow, with my one and only life, never again to go for gold.

Yet how can you put a price on beauty? Perhaps it's free.

But now I must let the beauty be and go to sleep at night.

Is that all nights are for? I ask myself.

Yes, they're for sleeping, I say to myself. You tried to turn night into day and you got beat.

There were so many nights. Nights when I wrote to the Stranger and danced with him.

Then, in the dark of that winter, the moon went sailing past the clouds, dropping her light through the twisty tree. There was the night when the snow came swinging down in half-circles through the light of the garden lamp, pattering soundlessly on to the sparkling ground. The tea in the blue and white cup was gold and so was the digestive biscuit. The music purring at three in the morning. Then it seemed that to be part of endless night might not be a bad idea.

The funny thing is that, as I write this, I know that two weeks from now I shall be at a place where I can at least try to tidy up my life. I so want to apologize for pestering someone; I can ask a man to give the Stranger a message.

I can hardly write a letter to say I'm sorry I wrote him so many letters.

I wonder if they sent them on from the radio?

Backwards and forwards I go, trying to remember, because when I have, I can forget. It was not good, it was not good. I fell in love with the pain in a man's eyes and it crucified me. Every aspect of it crucified me. I've read somewhere that it's one or the other – you either get crowned or crucified by love.

I don't know what it is any more.

'Love is a sickness,' Doctor Darling said once.

I keep thinking back to that last day. The day of the police. I wore my red hat like Frank Sinatra and my lipstick, all messy, and my black bra and pants. I had the music growling away.

'First we'll take Manhattan and then we'll take Berlin.'

I had to put my black shiny raincoat on when the doorbell rang; my neighbour wanted me to co-sign some legal paper. I felt so strange, so unwell. I signed it and she left. It must have looked frightening. Some of the photographs were torn up into little bits. The messages were on the windowsill for the cameras, and the black rooster was there too with all my jewellery hanging from the angles on him. My mother's pearls were round his neck. I had torn all the cigarettes to shreds and made a sort of tobacco soup. I had to make sure I didn't smoke them because they were all drugged. I poured all the Coca-Cola away and twisted the bottles. The music was thumping. Everything got blacker then and started to go even faster.

I thought my husband was a bigamist, a poisoner, a child molester and a thief. He'll take everything, I thought. I've got to stop him. I started ringing my accountant, ten times, twenty times.

'Sell my pension!' I screamed. 'Sell my pension!'

On and on, over and over. The secretary would put the phone down. I'd ring again. I could sense the panic of their office in my kitchen, but I didn't care, any more than I'd cared when I rang the school.

They keep telling me I was sick and I was, and it was so ugly, so ugly.

One explanation which I think even Doctor Darling wouldn't discount, funnily enough, came from my accountant later. He thought I'd been possessed by a devil. He's Indian. Perhaps they don't go in for bi-polar manic depression in India.

I went to buy some goldfish with my daughter when I wasn't well. I only wanted six, but there were seven. The only thing was, the seventh was such a little, ill-looking fish compared to the others.

'I can't just leave one behind,' I said. 'He'll be lonely.'

'Don't worry,' said the boy. 'Fish can only remember something for five seconds.'

'How do you know?' I said. 'Have you asked a fish? Or put electrodes on its head?'

He gave me a very funny look.

'Anyway,' I went on, 'you don't have to remember you're lonely – you just are.'

Who knows?

Maybe the doctor knows.

His were the only eyes that looked at me with respect when I was manic.

When he looked at me I could see that he was interested in me, and if not in me, then in my mind. I wasn't less than him just because I was ill. He was amused, which was startling. I felt a challenge coming towards me as our minds locked together. It was a battle of wills between equals. We were the same song but we were playing at different speeds. It was exciting. No one else ever looked at me like that.

'Your wife goes to places you and I have never been,' he said to my husband on one of our visits.

It was autumn. Check-up time had come round again. We were sitting in his office.

'How do you know so much?' I asked.

'I don't,' he said. 'I knew a patient here who said things would happen and they did.'

'What things?'

'I don't believe we have all the answers,' he said. 'Sometimes I ask younger doctors to question my diagnosis. It keeps me on my toes and my feet on the ground.'

I liked that. Here's someone at the top, I thought, and he's trying to go higher.

We walked home through the failing light. Beyond the trees I heard pipes. We walked on and there they were, two men standing still. One was playing the bagpipes.

'Look at that,' I said. 'I expect he's come out here to practise.'

'No, he's playing a lament for someone,' said my husband. 'Listen.'

'How do you know?' I asked.

'I just know.'

We listened, quite, quite still. We were just four in the park. The haunting music brought it all together. The deer, the birds, the leaves and the mud, the dying year.

So I was home now, no more part. I could still remember the lines, I'd turn them over in my head. I couldn't remember the fight though – how to do it.

The doctor thought it was providence that I drove myself to the only place that could help me. If I'd gone to work, to the theatre, either I might have decided the play needed rewriting while we were performing it, or they would have carried me out of the stage door screaming. But it didn't happen. I was lucky. I did my job. Nobody saw me doing my job badly. I was lucky.

I can't forget the dressing room. It was so pretty and so cosy. I had it to myself with my radio and my tiny TV. I even had a window-box. I'd forgotten all about that until this very moment. I wonder if it died? I'm sure not, someone would have taken it over.

All the bottles and scent and powder, the bits stuck on the mirror. The things that remind you of other shows. The card my kid once gave me.

For my mama, here is a picture of a owl.

The cards were so pretty and there were so many of them. One had pride of place. It was a drawing of a champagne bottle and a bunch of flowers sent by someone who had very nice writing, and it said 'Thinking of you.' I never knew who it came from.

It's so sad. I never said goodbye to any of them. I never

said sorry or thank you. It was unfinished and I miss them. I liked them.

I dreamt last night that I saw some of them walking towards me in a big space. They walked towards me holding broken sunglasses.

'You have to get these fixed,' they said. 'The play is going on.'

'Can I come back?' I asked.

'No, you can't,' they said embarrassedly.

'How does she play it?' I asked. 'Is she good?'

'She's wonderful,' one said. 'She's surreal.'

'Get the glasses fixed in five days,' said another.

I had to bury the part months ago but in a few days the play is coming off and that will be that. I loved that part.

When I first came out of hospital, one sweet actor sent me a card saying, 'Book me a room.'

We have such nice times. Contrary to what people think we do actually love each other. In thirty years you walk the wire with hundreds of friends and you talk, you don't make conversation. You get to know almost everything about them. You meet, you part, you meet again and there is love. Before you get a job there's jealousy and strife but then it disappears. When there's trouble, there's comfort. We know how to have a good time, and we don't need success to have it. I guess we're pretty lucky. We get paid to try 'to wake the soul with gentle strokes of art'.

I think things are meant. I have no choice but to think that. I feel so splintered because I caused so much pain. Yet some of the things I heard and felt made me melt into everything else.

Some of the things I saw were so beautiful. I know they were only hallucinations but they seemed pretty close to exaltation to me. I saw a floating face etched in golden light. I saw it three times and each time, as I ran towards it, it got further and further away.

I've been up before but never over the edge.

Only since I've been diagnosed have I understood that what I thought was normal is in fact manic depression. The snapping out of a depression is, on reflection, a palpable feeling, but I never recognized it as such at the time.

On the right-hand side of my brain it's almost as if I felt a liquid being secreted. A little shock, like a stretched elastic band snapping back slowly. Then, instead of the hopeless feeling of heaviness and inadequacy, there would be order and energy.

It happened twice when I cleared out cupboards. Virginia Woolf talks of this. It happened once in a car when I looked at flowers in a bed. Suddenly there was light and the fear was gone. Noradrenalin, serotonin. My brain producing chemicals as it should. It's like drawing a curtain back from a window, and in the light the ordinary things of life become extraordinary. Sunlight falling on a blue carpet, the warmth and comfort of coffee, newly washed hair, a cigarette. The minutiae of life become inexpressibly beautiful.

It was like being let out of prison. I was on the move again – out of the darkness. I never wondered at the fact that I couldn't keep still, not for a minute.

I read an article once about risk. Everyone is either high-risk or low-risk. HR or LR. HRs understand abstract paintings. LRs don't really like them.

I've got an abstract painting on my wall. It's a picture of a pink sky, a blue cloud, a white mountain, a diving-board and an oven-ready turkey.

'What!' said my husband. 'They're just colours.'

'No, look, can't you see?'

'So where's the oven-ready turkey?'

'There, in the snow.'

He took me to an exhibition. A private collection which included a Van Gogh.

'Look at that,' he said. 'That's not abstract.'

He'd painted such a lovely face, a face made of lines. The face of the nurse who'd cared for him at the hospital when he got high.

Afterwards we went to the National Gallery and saw the sunflowers.

'That picture makes me feel high,' I said. 'That's exactly what it feels like.'

'The man was in torment,' said my husband. 'Why do you like them so much?'

'It's because they're gold, I think. The brain goes gold. He painted heat. He makes me think about the other side of the sun. Who gets that heat?'

'Is that what it's like?'

'Yes, and sometimes when you're really tired and the rock and roll is thumping "Fuck the bullshit" it goes to diamonds. Have you ever seen diamonds by candle-light? They're fire and ice. The fire crackles and the ice cracks. Your head's full of crackle and crack. It's the World Cup.'

'It's that intense?'

'Yes, and now it's time to give it up,' I said. 'But I can't put my hand on my heart and say I wish I'd missed it.'

Sometimes when I think about where I went, my breath gets caught. But now, when I look at people, and I can tell that they've been there and back, I feel quite proud really.

I've got a tale too, I want to whisper, I've got a tale to tell too, but I won't.

You don't, but it's a sort of pact.

One of the overriding sensations in the high of a manic phase is a sense of exhilaration so intense that it is almost indescribable. One is suffused with it. I tried to feel it as a child in chapel, but could only do so if there was singing and candles and incense. But being Queen of the Sea needed none of those.

Sometimes I wonder at chapel, the crucifixion and God in a mood. I was taken aback at a fair once, when my two-year-old burst into tears at Punch and Judy. Perhaps she was too small to find pain amusing. Maybe she wasn't ready to keep it in the special, separate place.

I didn't know it then but I was high when she was born. I didn't sleep much and got the nesting instinct very intensely. I walked all the time to keep away from cigarettes.

The hospital was enough to make you high. A ward without sickness. A little scrap of heaven where you were at the furthest point from death and decay. The sun beamed in as we arrived. Everything seemed to be beaming. Men lolled – sheepish – happy to be redundant. Women in flowery gowns walked gingerly, looking beatific. Nobody rushed about. We seemed to be floating – waiting to change from two into three.

She slithered out and made little head butts on my stomach. I scooped her up and as she opened her mouth I fed her. I'd read it in a book. All animals have a rooting instinct for a few minutes just after they are born. If you catch them straight away they don't have to learn how to feed.

Mother's milk has a hundred parts. Cow's milk has six. I read that in a book too. And the hundredth part of mother's milk is a mystery. They don't know what it is. Magic. Unanalysable. Cow's milk for calves and magic milk for babies.

They took her away from me then. Why? But they brought her back. At least her first impression of the state of play hadn't been too bad. At least they hadn't held her upside-down and hit her.

The book said demand and supply. The more she drank of me, the more I had. I had so much that two young nurses came round with a cup.

'Could you spare some for the incubator babies?'

'Be my guest,' I said.

There was a milking machine so I went on that.

'The incubator babies nearest the door always thrive,' said a nurse. 'Whoever's passing by waggles their fingers and says hello. The babies at the back have to fight harder.'

The book said that babies and sensuality went together. Tiny little fat fingers and wrinkled wrists pressed against my flesh. But although it was sensual, it wasn't erotic. It was the way massage is akin to, but apart from, sex. Without the book I would have felt guilt at such pleasure. But why would nature have it otherwise? Why should making a baby be a separate feeling from feeding it? The relief and release at letting go of the tight feeling and the milk flowing away is pleasurable. It was gratifying and my waist was coming back a little more each day. She was getting fatter and I was getting thinner.

All this, and then the mysteriousness of whose skin belonged to whom. When I washed her, I seemed to feel my hands on my own skin – and when I washed myself, it seemed I was touching her.

I was so high and so tired and they wanted me to feed her at regular intervals. I tried that but I was so light-headed that I could never remember how much time had passed. I was sleepless and happy and we just rolled up together and I let her get on with it. Perhaps she had a small stomach and could only manage a snack at a time. She never cried – all the others did. Anyway I was cold for some reason, and there is practically no nicer sensation than a baby in the small of your back.

That was a lovely high but that was so long ago.

Everything has changed now. When you've been on the television people are very friendly. They tend to come into your space. It doesn't last very long, but while it does people are very chatty. Some days I used to really like it, other days I'd put my 'Sod off, I'm shopping' face on.

I don't do that any more. I look straight at strangers, especially as we walk, right into their eyes. They seldom speak and sometimes they look back, and when they do we smile. It's nicer this way.

I fell in love with the Stranger's face. I looked at a man's face and into his eyes on a screen and I believed in him.

If it doesn't begin, it can never end. That's what I wrote to him. It was a dream. It was a real dream though.

I think that probably, if I look deep into my soul, I just fancied him rotten, but I was too old and too married and so I had a nervous breakdown. It was either that or the pain of shattering my own dream of being a true-blue, vintage, loving, loyal wife; and I am, but not quite.

Can love be measured by loss? If something were to happen to the Stranger, how long would I grieve? But if I lost my husband, half of my life would be missing. I'd weep until my tears ran dry.

I think men can be wonderful. I think it is hard to be steadfast and resolute – it is for me. When someone believes in you, it helps. I believe in belief. I believe in honourable men. There can be no more worthwhile way to live than to love a man.

When some time had passed, my husband said that there was something understandable in it all, even that it was quite sweet. Except that he never used the word 'sweet'. Perhaps he'll remember the word one day and tell me.

I wanted a French wedding ring. I loved my wedding ring. I missed it. He bought it in the King's Road in '77.

We looked in all the *bijouteries*; they were all very clumpy and expensive. In the end we got one in Argos for £13.99. It's perfectly adequate and pretty too. It's a ring of little golden links that form a chain, but it was too big, so I had it made smaller, too small. It hurt like hell getting it on and I can't get it off unless I put soap all over my finger.

*　*　*

I don't think I'll ever speed again, not now I know about it. I'm so scared of it now. But it was so exciting. Lipstick and high heels, wine and men, songs and speed and dancing and dreams and black stockings, and last but not least, never, ever being bored.

Goodbye speed.

I tempted the gods when I drove so close and fast behind those big, smug cars. As I roared down the motorway that day I muttered bits of the Scottish play. I did it for the cameras. I said the spells. Someone once told me that they're real. They're real spells. Shakespeare used the real thing.

It was unwise.

I try to understand whether my howling sense of injustice is just the way I am or a symptom of manic depression. I don't know. All I know is that there were ways to escape when I was a child.

I could disappear into books and dreaming generally. I could make things happen so that I felt heroic, wanted and, above all, not bored.

I could sidle up behind toddlers playing at the edges of swimming pools and gently nudge them into the water. That was very gratifying because I could leap in shouting, 'I'll save you!' The mothers would be so grateful as I handed their screaming infants back to them.

Once, bored because the skating rink was too crowded for us to get on, I told a group of friends that the last time I'd been there were dozens of bloody heads rolling about on the ice. If you fell over and someone skated over your neck, they'd cut your head off. Again there was so much screaming.

I just liked making things up – just to see if I was believed. It was a good feeling, a good feeling after lights-out in the dorm – waiting to hear if Matron had finally padded away so that I could tell stories in the dark.

'Once in the far distance,' I told the sleepy girls in the dorm, 'once, just as day was turning into dark, a prince wheeled his horse to the right and set off to rescue her – his cloak billowing in the wind.'

Pause.

'Don't stop, don't stop, say some more!' said the voices in the dark.

'His eyes were chips of blue ice. Men quailed under their gaze, but they could melt like sunlit snow when he looked upon the woman he loved. He had a tortured past. He was the man in black.'

'What did she look like?' they asked.

'Me,' I said. 'But her hair was different. She had tresses of fire.'

'Do some more,' they begged.

I could say anything, turn the story any way I wanted, and they'd still believe me. Not only that, they'd pay me.

'I'll give you fifteen Maltesers,' said someone.

'Anyone else?'

'You can have half my banana chew.'

'What? Suck it and give it back?'

'It's my last one,' she said. 'I'll put it under the tap.'

'I've finished my sweets,' came a plaintive voice.

'You can pay me Saturday,' I said.

Everyone settled for the next instalment.

'She was wondrous to behold,' I resumed. 'But she had

a darker side. She was well versed in the black arts of poison and he was a little afraid of her . . .'

I saw a warlock on a chat show once. There was another man on with him. A man who had no time for warlocks. A man encased in cynicism. A man who knew no doubt. He talked and talked, on and on. The warlock didn't say anything for a long time. Then at last he spoke.

'So, you won't mind if I put a curse on you?'

The man minded.

It has stopped raining.

THE LOG

a short story

by

GRAHAM SWANNELL

1

'It's bugged,' she said.

'What?'

'The house is bugged.'

She looked elated. We were having a smoke in the kitchen at the time. It was a Friday evening in late April. It was after nine and the lights were on. She had also lit a candle. I was going on about politics. I was saying something about the bastards who were ruining the country.

'Ssh,' she went, putting her finger to her mouth.

'What is it?'

'They can hear us.'

'Who can?'

She giggled and switched on the radio. It was country and western music.

'You're cracking up,' I said.

But I was referring to her sudden infatuation with Nashville. I was in total denial about the bugging of the house. It just hadn't registered with me.

2

'Are you all right?' I asked.

It was early next morning and she was dancing to the music. She had a cigarette in one hand and her other hand was waving around her head.

'I see men everywhere,' she said.

'You've met someone,' I said abruptly.

She stopped and drank her coffee.

'You don't see women,' she said, refilling her mug with the strong ground coffee.

Outside it was a riot of colour. The birds were dashing about building nests. The sun was bouncing off the windows opposite. I put on the kettle to make tea.

'Who is he?' I asked.

'A marriage should be sacred and profane,' she said, 'but ours is only sacred.'

I noticed she had taken off her wedding ring and placed it on the windowsill.

'You're my brother not my lover,' she said.

She was right. It was true to say that recently we had not spent much time outside the temple.

'Well, it's . . .'

'I'm listening to Frank,' she snapped.

It was some Sinatra song like 'Fly Me to the Moon'. She had turned her back and was looking at the house opposite. She was utterly awake.

'I saw lights over there in the night.'

'You were up?'

'I was down here smoking and drinking coffee and the lights in that house were going on and off.'

'Really?'

Her eyes glittered. She looked as if she believed something special had happened to her. She reminded me of someone talking about a drug experience or a dream that was far beyond the ordinary.

I walked over to hold her. I wanted to earth her for a minute.

'Don't,' she said, putting her hand up like a traffic cop.

'Why can't I hold you?'

'They'll see.'

'What are you talking about?'

'He'll see.'

'Who?'

She smiled and lit another cigarette and looked out of the window. She was looking at the house where she had seen the lights. As she looked, she hummed along to the radio. It was some saccharine love song.

She's in love, I thought. That explains it. I felt my legs go. It was an effort to stay upright. I got to the table and sat.

'What the fuck's going on here?' I said. 'Who is this man? Are you having an affair?'

'I've never met him,' she said, as she left the kitchen and went upstairs to the bathroom. I heard the key turn in the lock.

3

'It's ice here for you,' she said later. 'You'd better go where it's warm.'

'This is my home,' I said. 'I have nowhere to go.'

'I know where you go. You can't fool me.'

I sat there staring at the green cloth that covered the table. I was picking at a piece of loose thread. She put on one side of *Imagine*. I hadn't heard it for years. It sounded strange.

'I want to leave you,' she said. 'I don't trust you. You're also very clever.'

'What?'

'You have guilty eyes.'

She was smoking furiously. She lit two huge blue candles and poured two glasses of red wine. I thought one glass was for me but she didn't offer it. Then I realized it was for the mysterious other.

'I am finally me!' she said, throwing her arms wide.

Then she changed the tape to Dire Straits and turned up the volume. It was so loud it made my eyes ache. It sounded as if there was a party going on in our house. She was so happy. She jigged about punching the air.

Then stopped and looked at me. Her eyes were wide and dark.

'I know where she lives,' she said.

'What are you talking about now?'

'Your other wife. The one you go to in the middle of the night. That's why you leave the hall light on all night. So you won't fall and break your neck. You think I don't know? I know everything.'

'You really are cracking up,' I said. 'I think you'd better go and see someone.'

'You want me to crack up.'

'How can you say that after all these years?'

'I'll crack up and then you'll be sorry.'

She turned and faced the wall and started muttering. It was a private conversation with herself. I had never seen her do that before. I got up from the table and started to move towards her. She turned and saw me coming and rushed out into the garden. I stood and watched her in the rapidly fading light. She was whispering to herself and pulling dead bits off a yellow plant. When she came back in she went and stood at the sink. She took a postcard on the windowsill and turned it round so that the card was facing the outside. She did that with another. She kept looking at the house opposite.

'If you didn't think I was having an affair,' I asked, 'would you still want our marriage to end?'

'Yes,' she said. 'I love him.'

'Why do you have to accuse me of having an affair when you don't want the marriage to continue anyway?' I asked.

'I don't trust you.'

She changed the tape, this time to Phil Collins. Then she launched into a speech about the right-wing establishment and how they had killed Buddy Holly, Lennon, Presley, Glenn Miller – her Soldiers of Song.

I stood there listening for a short while before the mist came down over my eyes and I ripped the tape out of the machine.

'I'm not listening to this!' I shouted. 'I refuse to listen to a guy who sent his wife a fax telling her that their marriage was all over!'

'Don't believe everything you read in the newspapers,' she said.

Then she went up to her bedroom.

I felt cold. I put on my coat but I was still cold. My teeth chattered for a time.

4

―※―

At 2.20 in the night I heard the downstairs door creak as she opened it. I had been meaning to oil it for years. The sharp, rasping sound pierced me.

I lay there trying to listen but all I could hear was a roar in my ears. The inside of my head felt like it was being scoured by coarse sandpaper. I tried to go back to sleep but failed. I felt an enormous weight pressing down on me in the bed. I lay there till four trying to make out what tapes she was playing. Then I got up and went downstairs and into the kitchen and I saw her.

I saw her for a split second and in that time I saw someone with lipstick all over their face making a mouth shape by kissing a piece of paper. At the end of that split second she spun round and saw me seeing her. She scrunched up the paper and wiped her face.

'I couldn't sleep,' she said. 'Do you want to go up to the park and watch the dawn?'

The kitchen was a mess. There were burnt pieces of newspaper sticking out of the bin, the contents of her handbag emptied on the table, congealed red candlewax on the white tiles of the windowsill, cigarette ash everywhere, photographs with parts torn off, more cards facing out by the window, writing in red lipstick on the window, a pile of tapes all out of their cases, her HRT packet facing out on the windowsill, along with something about Amnesty International and a biscuit tin with a photograph of Prince Charles, and a black metal rooster with her wedding ring in its beak, all facing towards the garden.

'I think you should go back to bed and try and get some sleep,' I said.

She turned up the radio.

'Did you hear what I said?' I shouted. 'This is getting out of control. If you don't sleep soon . . .'

'No one shouts at me!'

'I don't understand what's happening to us,' I said. 'This whirlwind has come from nowhere.'

'I know all about you,' she shouted back, putting on her coat. 'I know all about your other life.'

I went towards her to restrain her.

'Don't you touch me!'

Then she rushed out of the house and jumped into her car. She drove off with Bruce Springsteen at full blast.

I went back in and started to clear up. As I picked up the photographs, I noticed that I had been torn out of all of the ones that included both of us.

5

I was sitting there watching breakfast television when I heard the music and then finally the car pull up. She did not come in immediately; instead she sat in the car tearing up pieces of paper.

They said on the weather forecast that it was going to be the hottest day of the year so far.

Then she was in the house.

'I want you out of here!'

'What?'

'You heard me!'

'You're having an affair,' I shouted at her as she went through to the kitchen.

'I want you to leave,' she said. 'I do not trust you.'

'An affair is the only possible explanation for your behaviour.'

I said that, hanging back at the door. I had at least learnt something from previous occasions: I did not want a coffee mug whistling past my face. But this was not like anything I had known before. Before, I had been able to talk her down after a few hours. This time a shield had gone up that was impossible to penetrate.

'The trees moved,' she said.

Her mood had changed abruptly. She was softer, close to tears. She put on some lipstick.

'The what moved?'

'The trees.'

She stood in front of the mirror putting on thick lipstick. She ran her tongue around her lips when she had finished. She smiled at her reflection.

'Then the animals did what I asked.'

'What animals?'

I could not believe I had asked that question. I was allowing myself to be sucked into some kind of hallucination and was pretending that it was perfectly normal.

'I had this feeling that whatever I said, they understood,' she said. 'There was dew on the grass and I watched this big orange ball rise over the trees. It made me cry. I cried for us. I cried for all the good times we have had together. But what is the point of feelings in an unfeeling world?'

'Real feelings keep you from going insane,' I said.

'I know you want me to crack. Then you'll be happy. Oh yes, you'll be really happy then.'

The mood had swung again, back to the hard-edged. The face of stone. The fractured, shimmering eyes. She lit a cigarette and went and stood in the garden. I could see that she was talking out loud to herself. I was too far away to make out what it was she was saying. At one point she laughed and looked back to see if I was watching.

'You still here?' she asked as she came back and put on the radio.

Idiots were bantering with each other. Then there was a news broadcast. Someone had gone psychotic with an automatic gun. Then something about Europe, and finally some Royal piece about nothing at all. It sounded like another ordinary day except our marriage had hit the wall and was slowly dripping down it.

I sat at the table and could not hold it any more. Tears fell. They splashed down on my hands as I launched into a long statement about how it was all my fault. I suppose I thought that there must have been a reason for all the chaos and I assumed that reason was me. It did not occur to me that her dangerous state had absolutely nothing to do with me. That was something I didn't realize till later.

She came over to comfort me. She patted me. She thought about kissing me but walked off back to the sink. She was swaying to the music.

'I can't kiss you,' she said. 'I would be betraying him.'

'Let me get this straight,' I said. 'You are in love with a man you have never met?'

'He's an honourable man.'

'Oh, I'm sure.'

'He's married. I would never dream of coming between him and his family.'

'Have you had any contact with him?'

'I don't want to talk about it!'

'You have, haven't you?'

'I've written to him, all right!'

'Has he written back?'

She turned and faced the window. He obviously had not. At least someone was displaying a grain of common sense.

'I know what you're trying to do,' she said.

'What?'

'I know all about your little boy.'

Apparently I was still seeing my first wife and we had a little boy. I visited them in the night and when I went out for coffee at the Italian in the morning.

'Why don't we have coffee together any more?' she asked. 'We always used to have coffee together. Why do you need to go out for coffee? I know what you're up to.'

It felt like mid-winter. The embrace of a permafrost.

'If you love me,' she said, 'why don't you show it by really loving all of me? I can see that you know what I am saying is the truth.'

'Why are you so hard?' I asked. 'What have you got to be so distressed about?'

'You forget I was taught by masters!' she shouted. 'The nuns were unforgiving.'

An electrical force had taken hold of her. She sat. She stood up. She walked up and down. Words tumbling out of her angry mouth.

'How dare you try to undermine me! I found a photograph of some woman bending over the table and you were looking at her arse. I know what you were thinking. I've got to go, I've got appointments. I'm going to start my new life. Where's the Bible? I want to bone up on the New Testament. How dare they lock people up for twenty-three hours a day? Is that how they are going to reform? Look at your guilty eyes. I know the road where she lives. It's Lansdowne Road. I know the number. I know all about your shifty double life. Where's my credit card? Why do you buy this bottled water? I know you want to poison me. I'm being poisoned by this water. There's nothing wrong with tap water. I keep losing things. Where's my car keys? What have you done with my keys? You better go. There's nothing here for you. They even lock up women who can't pay their television licence. What kind of country is that? You judge a country by its health service. Where's my Enya tape? I know you've had every woman round here. He told me. He put me straight. He speaks to me. I hear him and he sees me. He can see me now on the camera. He is proud of me. He can see me standing up to you. I want you to go. There's no point in dragging this out. Go where you are loved. There is no love here.'

I packed a rucksack and went through the open door. She ran out after me.

'Aren't you going to say goodbye to me?' she asked.

'I'm innocent of all the charges,' I shouted at her from up the street. 'I'm an innocent man.'

6

I went to the doctor's and sat in the waiting room. I could not read the magazines.

'You look how I feel,' someone said.

'That good?' I replied.

The doctor was eating an egg roll. I explained in detail what my wife had been saying and doing. My mouth was dry all the time I was talking. I had to keep sipping water.

'I think she has a severe mental problem,' the doctor finally said as he finished his roll. 'It sounds like manic depression bordering on schizophrenia.'

'What?'

'I think I'd better go up and make an assessment.'

'What for?'

'Your wife must be hospitalized immediately.'

He picked up the phone and punched out our number. He wanted to be sure she was there.

'Hello, this is Doctor . . .'

I could hear the abuse from where I was sitting. Then I heard her slam down the phone. The doctor was shaken. His previous calm deserted him.

'I think we'd better get a section team together,' he said,

ashen-faced. 'I think the police should be in on it. They'd better pick out a couple of big boys. It sounds as if we're going to need them tonight.'

'What's a section?' I asked. It sounded draconian to me. My father used to section oranges with the precision of a surgeon. I kept thinking of a doctor I once knew who enjoyed slicing people open first thing in the morning. It made him feel on top of the world.

'Well,' said the doctor, 'you can have a Section 52, which means you can hold someone for seventy-two hours while you assess their mental health. If they are a danger to themselves or others you can then put them on a Section 2, which is for twenty-eight days, although that does not mean you stay the full time if you improve. There is also a Section 3 for treatment when they are forced to take the drugs.'

'Oh God,' was all I said.

While he was phoning up the various people who had to be involved – the welfare officer, the social worker, the psychiatrist, the police – he said that a psychosis was an invasion of the conscious by unconscious contents, so that the ego is partially or completely overwhelmed. What is commonly known as insanity. He said my wife sounded in the grip of a psychosis.

'It's common with a manic depressive,' he added.

'Is there any cure?' I asked, sinking further and further into my chair.

'No,' he said, 'they just take lithium and hope for the best.'

The phone rang. My mouth felt parched. Through the window I could see a pub. People were sitting outside clutching pint pots.

'Damn,' said the doctor, 'they can't find a psychiatrist. They're all out doing assessments. It can't be helped.'

It had never occurred to me that this kind of incident was happening to other people.

'We'll just have to wait,' he said. 'You'd better go and have a sandwich. This could take hours.'

I walked across to the pub but the music of Oasis was so loud it reduced me in seconds. I swallowed my drink and fled down to the river and sat on a bench next to a man in an overcoat. The sun was hot. The light cruel.

'They killed me mother,' said the man. 'It's terrible.'

He took out a can of Pepsi and lit a cigarette. He had difficulty in deciding whether to smoke or drink. Two ducks came up to the bench.

'What are them ducks doing there on the pavement?' he asked. 'Where did they fly in from?'

He searched his pockets, spilling Pepsi.

'No,' he said to one of the ducks who had come up to him, 'got no bread.'

The duck didn't move.

'I don't have any bread,' he said, this time close to tears.

The river was wide and swollen and ebbing. A flight of geese flew by, going low downriver. Over at the bridge a couple were kissing. Two old women with a dog came up from the towpath.

'I'm looking forward to my seeing my daughter and grandchildren,' said one. 'I shall just sit and wait for them to come.'

I thought of her at the house. I tried to imagine what she was going through there. I assumed all the mess was back in the kitchen and the music was at full blast. I could see the neighbours banging on the wall. I could see her taking a knife to herself. I could see all kinds of terrors and blood. I saw her being found with a knife in her chest and my only alibi the man sitting next to me.

'They killed me mother,' he repeated. 'It's terrible.'

The geese flew back upriver. Their wings creaked.

I crossed the road and made a call to an old friend and explained the situation.

'You must remain sane,' he said, 'and practical.'

'I am in a world without love,' I heard myself gibber. 'My heart is broken. Why has she done this to me?'

'She is not well,' came back his steady voice. 'If she doesn't get help, who knows what will happen?'

'Then I am making the right move?'

'There is no other,' he said. 'But you must look after yourself. You'll be no good to her if you crack. Are you listening to me? I know you.'

His voice started to penetrate.

'What's going to happen?' I asked.

'What will happen is the one thing you do not think will happen.'

I looked at the sex card in the phone booth. 'Demanding black leather and rubber lady. Very understanding for beginners. (Inferiors.) Call now.'

'She wants to be the child she was never allowed to be,' he said. 'She is probably in absolute bliss. Unaware of any of the consequences. Unfortunately you are all too aware.'

I was not sure.

'You'd better come over,' he said. 'I can sense you sliding all over the place.'

I said I had to go back to the surgery.

7

'She's already in hospital,' said the doctor. 'She was picked up by the police and taken to a psychiatric ward.'

His feet were resting on the desk. He had another egg roll on the go. The sunlight dappled the wall behind his head. A beatific grin spread across his face.

'She was found wandering around in a confused state,' he said. 'A neighbour phoned the surgery and we traced her for you. She is also using another name.'

It was her maiden name.

'At least there was no big fracas,' he said, 'which would have happened if we had had to admit her under section.'

'What do I do now?'

'What you must do is sit on your hands and wait.'

'I want to see her.'

'I do not advise you to do that,' he said, standing up and looking out of the window. 'You can go to the hospital by all means, but I recommend a meal, a bottle of good wine and a film. But make sure the film is not *The Madness of King George*.'

That cracked him up.

'Sorry,' he said. 'It just slipped out.'

I didn't take his advice.

I stood outside the ward. The door was locked. I looked through the small window in the middle of the door. I saw an old woman walking extremely slowly across what looked like a common room. She was bent forward and there were bandages around her legs and her feet were bare. She looked like a spectre – there was no one at home. I thought of pressing the bell but felt in need of a cigarette.

I walked away, passing a man coming up the centre of the corridor. He was gazing at the neon strip that ran all the way along the ceiling. He never took his eyes off it until he pressed the bell and was admitted to her ward.

Outside it was finally dark. I smoked and went home.

The house was a wreck. It was similar to the morning, but this time there was a cross in the window made up of a fish slice and a carving knife. There was a broken wineglass all over the floor. Written on the back of her tax return was: 'If I can't love him, I shall kill myself.' There was paper stuck to the window with messages that could only be read from the garden. I did not want to read them. There was also a large envelope already opened. Inside were ten or more letters. Two had been opened but the rest remain sealed. They were her letters to the man. I phoned the hospital.

'I'll do all I can, but she is very high,' said the nurse. 'She'll be all right though.'

He gave me a list of things to bring to the hospital the next day. Then there were other phone calls from social workers and doctors and they all asked if I agreed for her to be sectioned for twenty-eight days. I felt it was a great act of betrayal when I agreed to it. I packed the hospital bag in tears. Then fell asleep on top of the bed in my clothes.

The phone woke me the next morning.

'Get me out of here! I'm frightened! I don't like the drugs. They gave me an injection and orange medicine. I'm so frightened. I'll come home and take my medicine, just get me out of here!'

It was her voice. The voice of before. I had not heard that voice for so long. I had to tell her she had to stay to get better.

'What about those other women of yours,' she asked, 'and why do we never do anything together any more?'

I told her that I had never loved anyone except her. I told her that we would do things together in the future. I told her that she must sleep. She must give her racing brain a chance to rest. The nurse had said otherwise it would wear itself out.

'Phone tomorrow,' she said, when the nurse said she had had long enough on the phone.

I stood shaking in the bedroom. I could not control my hands. Then I changed and washed and shaved and left for the hospital. This time I rang the ward bell and entered.

There was a grey-faced girl with her mother saying, 'We'll come back, Julie.' A woman with one eye closed and ulcers on her legs saying, 'Would somebody help me.' Another woman, called the Countess, was asking someone, 'Are you coming back tonight?' When he said yes, she replied, 'Good.' Then there was an Irish woman who said, 'I'm going home.' She made a bolt for the door and three men came running out of a room and brought her back. She buried her head in her handbag and whimpered. 'Do you want two of your blue pills, Mary?' the nurse asked. There was another woman at the desk asking, 'Would someone help me with this teabag?' There was a black man reciting something about Malcolm X. Then he started doing karate kicks at some illusory person. A nurse told a patient to put out his cigarette. 'It wants to go for a walk,' said the patient, 'it wants some fresh air.'

They said it was too early to see her. I left the bag and caught a bus. A woman got on the bus. She had lank hair. She asked the bus driver if she was being good. Then she sat down and began to whimper. There was another, a youth, clutching a can of lager. He said, 'If only I could get steel-tipped Doc Martens.' He began to laugh. Then he started whispering to himself. People started getting off the bus.

The next day I phoned and asked if I could speak to her. She came to the phone but she had reverted back to the harsh voice.

'Why are you doing this to me? Why am I locked up? I want to get out. I did nothing wrong. I am not a danger to anyone. You have put me away. Why? Where is my father's gold watch? I know all about you. I know all about your life!'

'The doctor said . . .'

'Why do you believe the doctors? Get me out of here!'

The phone went dead.

8

On the Wednesday I was allowed to see her. The taxi driver talked to me in his mirror.

'I put a fiver, which I could ill afford, on the first race, but it failed to show,' he said.

'I know the feeling,' I said.

She was in a little room. She was lying in bed and she looked bad. Her skin was grey and the right side of her mouth was drooping and saliva was dripping out. She stretched out her arm and I could see dark bruises below the elbow.

'Needles,' she said.

I poured her a glass of water and she sipped it. The drugs made her thirsty.

'Why am I in here?'

What I said did not register.

'The trees moved and the animals understood me,' she said slowly. 'The horses turned their heads and listened to me.'

Someone came in and gave her a pill and she went off to sleep. It was calm in the room. The vortex was gone.

The next day it was back.

She was sitting on the floor in her dressing-gown. She was reading the paper and smoking.

'You put me in here, didn't you?'

'I signed nothing,' I said.

'There is nothing much to say, is there?'

She went and started playing cards with the other patients in the common room. I passed them on the way out and she never looked at me.

The nurse said the patients take the lithium for a time, say three months, then they stop and usually return to the ward.

I went to the library and read up on it. I had decided that someone was going to have to tell her the facts and that person was going to be me.

She phoned on Friday at 7.24 in the morning. She wanted her shampoo and boots.

'I want to get dressed today.'

'I'll come at eleven.'

'I've nothing to say to you.'

She was sitting on a bench in a small garden. She looked frail. The bright sunlight made her skin even whiter. She was holding a twig.

'You are suffering from manic depression,' I said. 'Have they told you this yet?'

She shook her head.

'It is pretty much a mystery. It could be genetic, it could even be a birth trauma. Who knows?'

'I don't want to know,' she said.

'In the manic phase you are subject to wild delusions that you believe to be absolutely true. You start writing reams of stuff to people or to yourself; some people go on shopping sprees and empty the bank; wild struggles go on inside you, flights of ideas about life and religion race through your mind at breakneck speed. You also hallucinate and you are subject to delusions of all kinds.'

'The voice said I was being poisoned,' she said. 'It was so real.'

She was peeling the bark off the twig.

'Go on,' she said.

'The mania is followed by the depressive phase. This is as inevitable as night following day. This is black and hopeless and full of despair and a sense of utter worthlessness. That is the cycle. The lithium is supposed to prevent the cycle from kicking in again. Unfortunately this cycle has to run its course because there is no way of stopping it.'

The birds were singing. The dew on the grass had dried. There was a high thin sheet of cirrus above our heads. It felt like the first day of the rest of our new life.

'Thank you for telling me,' she said.

9

We stood at the desk waiting for some discharge papers. The nurses were joking with her. They did not want to see her again. She said she did not want to see them either. Then one of the nurses told her that she was lucky to have someone who cared for her. She smiled at the nurse.

'He's been a wonderful friend to me through all this,' she said to the nurse.

She didn't mean me.

Afterword

❧❦☙

Diamonds Behind My Eyes is a remarkable account of what is known as Manic Depressive Illness, a medical condition afflicting nearly 1 per cent of the population. It has two dramatic faces, like the bright and dark sides of the moon.

In the manic phase, the brain is racing until its spins out of control. Thoughts come cascading out, with irresistible pressure, until reason is drowned in the torrent of swirling ideas. The mind loses its balance and generates garbage data. The senses are heightened, there is rising optimism, over-confidence, and often an exaggerated mood of romance that is compelling and all-consuming. Because the mental linkages are so fast, other people's thinking seems pedestrian, and the consequent impatience and irritability is a hallmark of the condition. Any suggestion that this active, super-charged state could be an illness is naturally dismissed out of hand. As Sigmund Freud put it so well, 'Illusions commend themselves to us because they save us pain and allow us to enjoy pleasure instead. We must therefore accept it without complaint when they sometimes collide with a bit of reality against which they are dashed to pieces.' The pleasure is intense and the illusion is that it can go on for ever; therefore when reality intrudes there is an explosion of complaint.

The human brain has a design fault: the more tired it gets, the more elusive sleep becomes. The manic depressive does not have enough time for sleep, to allow the brain to recharge its batteries. Emotions may then fluctuate wildly, and there are delusions, even hallucinations. There is no hand on the mental helm, and in the end the ship hits the rocks and begins to sink.

The mood which was comet-bright as it sped across the sky goes into burn-out, and begins to fall like a stone. There is an overwhelming sense of dread, and a fear that something awful is about to happen. Storm clouds gather and the mind is full of dark imaginings. Tearfulness, self-doubt, guilt, pessimism and hopelessness overwhelm the victim of depression. This is a major illness which can be life-threatening: if life is not worth living, suicide may seem the best option.

Depression can afflict the most talented of people, and often strikes perfectionists. Normally able to cope so well, they are suddenly robbed of their confidence and mental ability; memory is impaired, concentration becomes difficult and the libido vanishes. The well-meaning advice to 'pull yourself together' implies that the depressed person is just not trying, and completely misses the point – if somebody is bleeding to death, you have to stop the haemorrhage, not lecture the victim.

Fortunately there are many ways to treat depressive illness. Anti-depressants do several things: they can restore normal sleep; reduce anxiety and panic attacks; and slowly lift the mood – though at first this is erratic:

three steps forward and two back. Tearfulness lessens and the appetite returns. Anti-depressants are not habit-forming, and they can be life-saving, yet often sufferers are too proud to accept them. But most people do not assume they can heal their own stomach ulcer without drug therapy, and the brain is infinitely more complex than the stomach; so, if the neurotransmitters are out of balance to the extent that they cause mania or depression, healing should be accelerated with anti-depressant drugs. Lithium carbonate, which is not an anti-depressant but a mood stabilizer, if given in the right doses, which can be monitored by blood tests, can prevent further attacks of depression and/or mania. Also, counselling and the support of friends and family can prove invaluable. The Samaritans have saved countless lives; Depression Alliance and the Manic Depression Fellowship are two self-help groups who are only too willing to offer intelligent advice.

This splendid book will, I believe, help many to understand the courage required to do battle with Manic Depressive Illness. It is a battle worth winning, for few things are as important as to be at peace with oneself.

Desmond Kelly
Visiting Professor of Psychiatry, University College
London 1997

For further information and advice, please contact the Manic Depression Fellowship on 0181–974–6550 or Depression Alliance on 0171–633–9929.